THE CLASS OF '57

A gutty saga of "higher" education

by Jerry Harju
'57 Engineering, University of Michigan

THE CLASS OF '57

A gutty saga of "higher" education

by Jerry Harju
'57 Engineering, University of Michigan

Illustrations by
Rick Humphrey

Copyright 1997
by Jerry Harju
and Avery Color Studios

Published by Avery Color Studios
Marquette, Michigan 49855

Printed in Michigan, U.S.A.
by Lake Superior Press
Marquette, Michigan 49855

ISBN 0-932212-97-2
Library of Congress Card No. 97-068445

September, 1997

Introduction

This book is about higher education—mine. Some of the education was formal—some informal. Some against my will—some welcomed. Some expensive—some free of charge. *All* of it was invaluable, as education usually is.

It's a narrative—often humorous—of my days at the University of Michigan, where I pursued a degree in engineering. University life then—with its 1950's attitudes on world affairs, morality, women's roles in society, and other matters—was much different from today. I've tried to capture the flavor of the times.

Neither my mother nor my father had the opportunity to finish high school, so they both knew first hand the problems *no* education can bring. During my high-school years, they tried to tell me this, but at that age I was too dense and shortsighted to see the big picture. I resisted going to college, but my parents insisted.

Throughout the book I refer to my father as "the old man." This isn't a show of disrespect. It was the venacular of the time—especially in Upper Michigan where the story begins. His English was fractured and his vocabulary limited, but my father had more common sense and insight into the human condition than anyone I've ever known.

Some of the story is about my engineering-student co-op job at White Sands Proving Ground during the earliest days of United States missile development when *nobody* in this country was a rocket scientist.

By nature I'm a writer of humor, so I don't want you to think that this is a serious treatise on technical higher education. Much of the *real* education I received was neither technical nor high level. I hope you'll enjoy reading about it.

Jerry Harju
1032 Northland Drive
Marquette, MI 49855

Dedications

To my parents, who made all this possible.

To Andy McNamee, my beloved cousin who was taken from
us before his college days.

Acknowledgements

As always, there are many people whose assistance made this book possible.

If you think that all the words in this book are mine, it's not true. Pat Green, my girlfriend who has helped me through four books, and Karen Murr, my clever cousin, are both masters of the English language and very capable editors. They have contributed substantially by correcting punctuation, substituting words, and generally making the prose much more readable. Rick Humphrey has once again produced a set of charming drawings, including the cover illustration. I thank Dick Beaudry, a fellow University of Michigan classmate, who diligently read the manuscript and kept me honest on 1950's U of M miscellany. Finally, I thank Jeff, Kim, Monteal, Libby, Chris, Cam, Harriet, Mike, Roger, and Dr. Hatcher who reviewed all or part of the manuscript.

Other Books by Jerry Harju:

NORTHERN REFLECTIONS

NORTHERN D'LIGHTS

NORTHERN PASSAGES

Contents

The Old Man

January 19, 1951

Friday, January 19th, 1951
Marquette County, Michigan

*I*t was cold—*damn* cold.

I eased my 1930 Model A Ford down Highway US41 at thirty-five miles an hour, sedately heading east to Marquette, Michigan. The car had bald tires, a leaky radiator, and bad steering, and that was about as fast as I cared to drive it in twenty-five-below-zero weather. Bundled up in our heavy mackinaws, my old man and I filled the front seat of the narrow Ford. We had the whole road to ourselves—everyone else had the good sense to stay inside when it got this cold.

The Ford's manifold heater was totally inadequate for the job, not even warming the incoming air to above freezing. The old man, who had never driven a car and who possessed zero knowledge of anything automotive, kept kicking the heater port in the firewall with his swamper boot, trying to induce it to throw out more heat.

"Pop, y'wanna break out that coffee?" I asked.

The old man unscrewed the cap from the big thermos. The heat gushed out in a big cloud, fogging up the right side of the windshield. He poured some coffee.

"Y'know," I said. "I hear them tool'n die makers down in Milwaukee are makin' *eight* dollars an hour."

"Whut th'hell," he retorted. "Y'think ya kin jus' go t'Milwaukee an' be a tool'n die maker? Crissakes, it'd take ya longer t'learn *that* than gettin' a college degree."

"Mebbe, but at least I'd be gettin' a paycheck while I'm learnin'."

"Look, ya got plenty a time later t'worry 'bout money. We'll get ya through college somehow. Don' ferget, we still got them war bonds t'cash."

I was going to graduate from high school in the little Upper Michigan town of Republic in June. The University of Michigan was conducting an open college-scholarship examination that afternoon in Marquette, and my mother and the old man had decided that I should take the exam.

I shook my head skeptically. "Michigan's gonna cost a bundle, I bet. Even if they gimme th'tuition with this scholarship, I gotta stay at a dormitory... they feed ya all yer meals... that ain' gonna be cheap. Besides, I don' even know whut kinda degree t'get."

I'd had enough of school. College meant nothing more than another four years of plowing through dull textbooks—and worse, another four years of being broke. After jerking sodas and washing dishes in my folks' little eight-stool, three-booth restaurant for the princely sum of five dollars a week, I was ready to grab my high school diploma, scoot down to Milwaukee, and make some real money for a change.

My parents quickly squelched that idea. They'd spent their whole lives laboring at logging camps, potato farms, and now this tiny restaurant. They were relentless about my college education, whether I wanted one or not. Heated arguments hadn't budged them. In fact, the old man was riding shotgun that morning to make certain I actually went to the exam.

He blew on his coffee and took a slurp. "Y'always liked airplanes. Why don'cha get a degree where ya kin design airplanes?"

I pounded my left foot on the floorboard to warm it up. "Hah! Kin you see anybody lettin' *me* design an airplane?"

He passed the hot coffee over to me. "I dunno whut t'tell ya. All I know is at least ya'll get down inta civilization. If ya don't, ya'll wind up diggin' iron ore up here jus' like yer uncles."

I was getting irritated. "I keep tellin' ya... I wanna go t'*Milwaukee*, an' *that's* civilization. I kin make big money down *there*... without minin'."

"Look," he said. "Four more years a school ain' gonna hurt ya. Then, anyway—with a college degree—ya kin pick'n choose from a better class a work."

"Whut do *you* know 'bout college?" I said hotly. "Ya didn' even get through the sixth grade." I immediately regretted saying that, knowing he'd had to quit school to go to work.

A couple of years ago he would have clobbered me for mouthing off like that, but this morning he didn't seem to be offended at all. Instead, he barked out a laugh. "Well, yer right 'bout that. I don' know nuthin' 'bout college, or any kind'a education, fer that matter."

This was the old "I never had nothing when I was young, but I want to see you get a chance" sermon he recited to me every so often. I was already tuning it out when he suddenly took a different tack, continuing in a forceful voice that rose above the clatter of the Model A's engine.

"Tell ya whut I *do* know sumthin' about, though. *No* education! *No* education is hitchin' up a team a horses out in the woods before the sun comes up and it's twenty-five below—like it is this mornin'—but ya can't go inside an' warm up 'cause ya hafta drag logs 'cross the snow all day. *No* education is sweatin' yer ass off all summer growin' potatoes that nobody kin buy, an' ya wind up givin' 'em away or tradin' 'em fer somethin' else t'eat 'cause yer tired of eatin' potatoes alla time. *No* education is havin' t'mop up the mess when some drunken pulp-cutter staggers into th'restaurant late at night and throws up on yer clean floor. Ask me anythin' ya want 'bout *no* education, boy. I'm a gawdamn expert on that."

I could feel his eyes burning into me as I stared out the frosty windshield. We continued the trip in silence.

The Freshman Year
A Struggle for Survival

**The University of Michigan
September 1951 - June 1952**

Sunday, September 16th, 1951
Ann Arbor, Michigan

I got off the train at the Ann Arbor railroad depot lugging my suitcase and an A&P shopping bag. Navigating the steep hill on State Street raised a pretty good sweat. Wearing my woolen high school graduation suit didn't help, but there wasn't anyplace else for it except on my skinny frame.

The shopping bag was full of my underwear, a half-empty thermos of coffee, and leftover roast-beef sandwiches. Yesterday, as my mother packed the sandwiches into the bag, she warned me to stay out of the dining car, claiming that I had better things to spend my money on than buying food from the railroad.

By the time I got to the intersection of Liberty and State, at the edge of the University of Michigan campus, foot traffic had picked up considerably. Students were noisily crowding into the stores, buying up whatever college students had to buy. Slater's Bookstore was mobbed with kids waving books and money in the air.

Further south on State Street, the stores disappeared, replaced by stately brick and granite campus buildings set well back from the street. The mammoth-columned portico of Angell Hall added to the aura of scholastic sobriety.

I was feeling small and lonely. Republic High School had a total student enrollment of one hundred and twenty-five. The University of Michigan had fourteen thousand—more than the population of Marquette, the largest city in Upper Michigan.

Some guys were hanging out the upper-story windows of a large brick mansion (a fraternity house, I found out later), noisily heckling pedestrians. One of them saluted me with his glass of beer.

"Welcome to the big city," he yelled. The rest of them laughed raucously.

The A&P shopping bag was a dead giveaway. I stopped, quickly folded the top of the bag over and crammed it under my arm, trying to disguise it.

"Welcome to the big city," he yelled.

This was humiliating—I hated the place already. If I had used my head, I would have purposely blown that scholarship exam in January, because the next thing I knew, I was awarded four years of tuition to the University of Michigan. My course was set.

I found the West Quadrangle—a huge, half-a-square-block, red-brick fortress that housed eight men's dormitories. The lounge in Allen Rumsey House, the dormitory where I was destined to sweat out my freshman year, was in a state of turmoil with dozens of guys in the process of moving in. Early-arrivals were sprawled on sofas watching television.

My gawd—television! Most of the Upper Peninsula couldn't get television reception at all. Holding the suitcase and shopping bag, I stood transfixed. On the tiny black-and-white screen some guy was sweating in the midday sun, trying to sell used cars off a lot somewhere in Detroit.

"And who might you be, young man?"

I tore my eyes away from the car commercial to find a short, plump, matronly woman giving me a businesslike once-over. I gave her my name, and she moved her finger rapidly down a list on her clipboard.

"Oh, yes... room three-oh-nine. Welcome to Allen Rumsey House," she said dryly. "I'm Mrs. Harper, your housemother. You stay right here. I have to get a couple of boys settled into their rooms on the second floor, but I'll be back for you in a few minutes."

She could have taken all day if she wanted. I had no trouble at all killing time watching television. The commercial ended and two guys in a boxing ring appeared. They were wrestlers, but this was wrestling like I'd never seen before. One guy threw the other to the canvas and began jumping up and down on his stomach. The referee tried to step in and got smacked in the head for his trouble. I couldn't believe it. Hitting a referee—jee-suss!

This didn't faze the other guys in the lounge. They hooted and whistled, yelling at the guy on the canvas to get to his feet and get down to some *real* wrestling.

The housemother returned and dragged me away from the television set. I followed her up the stairs with my baggage.

"Woman on the floor," she bellowed as we got to the third-floor landing.

"Did your parents bring you to Ann Arbor?" Mrs. Harper asked.

"No, ma'am, I took th'train."

"Then, after you get settled in your room, call them right away and let them know you arrived safely."

"They don't have a telephone, ma'am," I replied. "I'll write a letter today."

She rapped on the door of room 309 and without waiting for a response, opened it.

The dorm room was bigger than my bedroom at home, but it already had two other guys living in it.

"This is Robert Buttram and Murray Rosenkranz," Mrs. Harper said, waving her hand at the two occupants. They both wore thick glasses, and it would be several days before I could tell them apart.

We shook hands. Rosenkranz, squinting through the smoke of a cigarette dangling from the corner of his mouth, said, "Last to arrive gets the top bunk."

The room was crammed with furniture: three sets of cheap wooden desks and chairs—one single bed and a metal, double bunk bed, each covered with an army surplus, woolen blanket—and two small dressers painted olive-drab to match the blankets.

Mrs. Harper handed me several sheets of paper. "Here are the house rules. Dinner is at six sharp... coat and tie. Robert's a sophomore; he'll show you where the dining room is." She abruptly wheeled around and left the room.

My roommates pointed out my allotted twelve inches of hanger space in the only closet, as well as the two dresser drawers that were exclusively mine.

"Whut's a housemother?" I inquired as I stashed my belongings.

Buttram asked, "You read Orwell's *1984*?"

"Uh... nope."

"*1984*'s a science fiction novel set in the future. In it, Big Brother watches everybody, day and night. Mrs. Harper's our Big *Mother*, and she watches everybody, day and night, t'make sure we don't sneak girls in our rooms for sex orgies."

I took in the crowded room and the eighteen-inch-wide top bunk where I would be sleeping. A sex orgy in here would require awfully skinny women.

"What are you?" Rosenkranz asked me.

"Whut am I? Whaddaya mean?"

"I'm Engineering '55," Rosenkranz said. He jerked his thumb at Buttram. "He's Music '54. A sophomore."

"Oh... I'm Engineering, Class of '55—same as you."

Rosenkranz was happy to see that he was rooming with a fellow fresh-man engineer. "Buy your slide rule yet?"

I stared blankly. "Whut?"

He produced an oblong leather case. From it he extracted an odd-looking device—a foot-long ruler designed by aliens. It was made of three parallel strips of wood—the middle one movable—and a sliding glass window; the whole thing was covered with tiny numbers and graduations.

"It's a Post Versalog... the best you can buy," Rosenkranz said proudly. He held it under my nose for closer inspection. "Real imported bamboo." Then he snapped open a leather loop on the slide-rule case and mounted it on his belt. It looked like a long-barrelled gun holster. "Pretty handy, huh?"

"He's the fastest logarithm calculator in the Old West," Buttram chuckled.

I silently put my socks and underwear in a dresser drawer, idly wondering what a *log rhythm* was.

Monday, September 17th, 1951
The Michigan Union

Today was the start of Orientation Week, time to acquaint freshmen with the campus, give physical examinations, and get us registered for classes. I had explicit, written instructions guiding me through every minute of every day for five straight days. At eight a.m. sharp I was to report to a room on the second floor of the Michigan Union building.

The Union had the atmosphere of a gentlemen's private club, with dark wood paneling and large crystal chandeliers. One expected to see old fogies sitting in the heavy, leather-upholstered chairs, reading the financial news, but this morning the Union was teeming with freshmen scurrying in all directions. The room on the second floor was already crowded with some thirty guys.

My graduation suit was considerably more formal than the prevailing dress code. Many of the guys were wearing curious-looking white-suede shoes. The white-shoe people tended to talk only to one another—some kind of club, I figured. I later found out the shoes were called white bucks—very much in style and very expensive.

A handsome, deeply tanned guy dressed in a crisply starched white shirt, gray flannel slacks with razor-sharp creases, and, of course, white bucks marched up to the podium at the front of the room. He held up his hands for silence.

"Good morning. I'm Jack Radcliff—Engineering '53. I'll be your orientation leader throughout the week." He grinned, the light from the chandelier glistening off his toothpaste-ad, perfect teeth.

"All of you are Engineering '55. This makes it easier to acquaint you with the areas of the campus where you'll be spending most of your time. You'll notice that there are no women in the group... after all, we're engineers." Then he added with a confidential half-smile, half-leer, "But that doesn't mean your social life will wither. Twice a day we'll be taking *mixer breaks*, so you'll have plenty of opportunity to meet women."

Radcliff let that revelation sink in as he fished out a knobby briarwood pipe, filled it with tobacco from a soft leather pouch, and expertly lit it with a gold lighter. Some of the other white-buck guys immediately brought out pipes and began to stoke them up.

"Before we get started this morning," Radcliff continued, "do you know what you *are*, as of this moment? Anybody?"

No one spoke up.

"You're *Michigan Wolverines*!" Radcliff cried. "And when we walk around the campus this week I want you all to throw your shoulders back and show some Wolverine pride! Let's go!" He quickly headed for the door.

A Michigan Wolverine. I savored the thought as we followed Radcliff out of the room. I had never seen a wolverine, but I'd heard they were bad customers, able to beat the crap out of everything else in the woods. I threw my shoulders back.

Radcliff gave us a quick tour of the Union, the billiard room on the second floor and the barber shop, swimming pool, and four-lane bowling alley in the basement.

Outside, Radcliff brought the group to a halt at the Michigan Union front entrance on State Street. "I'm going to start your education right now."

He pointed up the steps at the Union. "The Union is an exclusive club for Michigan *men*. It's *your* club. When you bring a woman into the Union you *must* use the side door over to the right. *Women are not allowed to use the main entrance of the Union.* Understood?"

It made perfect sense to all of us, and we nodded wisely. After all, we couldn't let just *anyone* walk into our club—especially through the front door. In two columns, we stepped out smartly down South University Avenue, trailing great plumes of pipe-tobacco smoke behind us.

Over on East University Avenue we toured the engineering buildings. Deep in the bowels of the West Engineering building we were shown huge machines that engineers used to break things that other engineers had designed. We viewed the large water tank that naval-architecture engineering students used for sailing and testing boat models. We marvelled at the quaint antiquity of the red-brick exterior of East Hall, built as an elementary school during the post-Civil War era.

After visiting the physics buildings we proceeded over to the Michigan League, the women's equivalent of the Union. Radcliff ushered us into a large cafeteria whereupon he immediately struck up a conversation with a good-looking blonde. After a few words he came back over and gathered us into a huddle.

"Okay men, this is our first mixer break," he said quietly. He pointed to a large group of unattached girls sitting at tables near the far wall. "See those women? Go over there, pick one out, find out what she wants to drink, and get her name and telephone number. We've only got thirty minutes, so get to it." Having issued orders to his troops, Radcliff returned to the blonde—the female orientation group leader—and led her to an empty table.

The operation was clear. We had established a beachhead and our mission was to storm out and engage the enemy.

The white-bucks clearly had more stomach for this, whipping out address books as they quickly approached the girls. By and by, the rest of us tentatively followed.

I was paralyzed with fright. The few girls I had dated in the Upper Peninsula, I'd known for years. On occasion, a few of us studs had driven to neighboring towns to cruise around on the pretext that we were bored with the Republic girls. It amounted to nothing more than slowing down and making suggestive comments to the girls on the sidewalk as we drove by.

"Go over there, pick one out, find out what she wants to drink, and get her name and telephone number."

None of us ever mustered up the nerve to actually make a date with a strange girl.

By the time I edged over to the freshmen girls, all the good-looking ones had been taken. The ones left were in a peevish mood because they hadn't been selected. I gingerly approached a sour-looking, round-faced girl sitting by herself.

"Uh... hi," I said glibly.

"Don't feel obligated," she snapped.

"Whut?"

"Don't feel obligated to pick me up."

"Oh... no... no... it's fine with me. I'm happy t'pick ya up." *That didn't come out right.*

"This whole mixer thing stinks," she said waspishly. "Why don't they quit wasting our time and just get this orientation business over with? I've got more important things to do... like getting over to Slater's Bookstore." She drummed her fingers impatiently on the empty table.

I remembered that I was supposed to ask her what she wanted to drink. " Kin I buy ya a cuppa coffee... a Coke... anythin'?"

"Well... as long as I'm stuck here for awhile... I'll take a strawberry sundae."

Strawberry sundae?—damn, one with expensive taste. I went up to the counter and got the sundae, plus a cup of coffee for myself. The coffee was steaming hot, and I almost poured some into the saucer to cool it off— Upper Peninsula style—but caught myself. With a grumpy look, the girl ate the sundae in silence.

Radcliff came over and snapped his fingers, indicating the mixer was over. The men got up and followed him out. Neither the strawberry-sundae-eater nor I had any burning desire to exchange names and telephone numbers.

"I got *two* names and phone numbers," said one of the white-bucks.

"I got *three*," cried another.

"Excellent!" Radcliff exclaimed, closely inspecting the two with an appraising eye, no doubt considering them as potential candidates for his Sigma Nu fraternity. He'd let it slip during the morning tour that major-league ladies men were in strong demand at Sigma Nu.

We toured the chemistry building, then broke for lunch. I trudged back to the dormitory dining hall where I was introduced to the infamous West-Quad lunchtime fare of grilled-cheese sandwiches and tomato soup.

The sandwiches had the texture of sweat socks. Of course, what I didn't realize was—this being Monday—they were relatively fresh and tender. The survivors would congeal into a truly impenetrable mass before being served again on Friday.

At two in the afternoon the Radcliff team once more intercepted a female orientation group in the Michigan League cafeteria. This time I screwed up my courage and moved in faster, snaring a busty brunette with pouty lips.

"Hi... kin I get ya a cuppa coffee or a Coke?" I rattled off nervously.

She bathed me with a fetching smile. "Why, yes," she said in a syrupy Southern drawl. "A cup of coffee would be nice."

This was more like it. I briskly brought two coffees over and sat down. The muscles in my jaw ached from the grin frozen on my face, advertising that I was a very congenial fellow who she should get to know better.

She took a delicate sip of coffee. "Your orientation group is pre-law, is that right?"

"Whuts that, y'say?"

"Ya'll are going to be lawyers, aren't you?"

"Oh, no. We're gonna be engineers."

Her smile evaporated. "Oh... dear... ah'm sorry. No... no... ah mean ah would have sworn that Gloria—she's our group leader—said that ya'll were going to be lawyers." She lowered her eyes, gazing into her coffee mug as she attempted to mask her disappointment.

My mind frantically rummaged around for something brilliant to say to salvage the conversation. Finally, in desperation I blurted out, "So, whut're *you* gonna major in? Heh, heh." *Brilliant.*

"Oh... ah haven't rightly decided. Ah expect to be spending most of my time entertaining my future husband's clients. Ah haven't seen anything like that in the course catalogs, though."

She stared intently at each of the boys in Radcliff's orientation group, trying to determine if there were any budding Einsteins among us. "Ah'll give it more thought later in the week when ah register for classes. Right now ah've got to think about which sororities ah want to rush."

My mind went totally blank. How do you respond to career goals like that? I parboiled my upper lip taking a huge gulp of hot coffee in the hope that a jolt of caffeine would inspire me. Nothing. For several minutes we just sat there like two lumps.

Finally, she stood up. "It's been real nice talkin' to ya'll, but ah think ah'll wait for the group outside." She hurried out the door.

Before dinner that night, I told my troubles to my roommates.

"Whut'm I gonna do?" I moaned. "I can't think a nuthin' t'say t'these girls at th'mixer breaks and this's gonna go on all week!"

Buttram was in the middle of our room, pounding the floor with his feet, practising his rapid-fire, high-stepping daily marching exercises—knees thrashing upward toward his chin, like pistons. He was a tuba player in the University of Michigan Marching Band and had to get his legs in shape for the band's trademark 180-steps-per-minute march used when entering the football stadium.

He stopped and mopped his face with a towel. "Had the same problem myself during Orientation Week last year," he confided. "You need a script."

"A script?"

"Yeah. You'll never see the same girl twice, unless you wanna make a date, right?"

"I guess so."

"So you write a script of what you're gonna say to a girl, memorize it, and tell them all the same thing. Sprinkle in some questions to show you're interested in them. Once you get the hang of it, it's easy—you don't even have to think. Don't make it too long, though. You wanna keep it short enough so you can talk to two or three of them—one after another—in a half-hour."

It was pure genius. That night I stayed up into the wee hours composing my dialogue.

Tuesday, September 18th, 1951
Waterman Gymnasium

I didn't get an opportunity to test my ingenious girl-script immediately. Tuesday morning was booked for the university's physical exam. I'd never had a physical, but from what I had seen at the movies I imagined a kindly, gray-haired doctor putting a wooden stick on my tongue, telling me to say "Ah," listening to my heart, and pronouncing me physically fit to be a Michigan Wolverine.

Our orientation group met again at the Michigan Union and trooped over to Waterman Gym on the corner of North University and East University Avenues. There we merged with a thousand or more male freshmen scheduled for physicals. We filed into the gym and were directed to line up to retrieve our paperwork, including the medical questionnaires we'd filled out and sent in months ago.

Four Republic High School gyms could have fit inside Waterman Gym—it had several basketball courts across its width. The high ceiling was supported by a maze of steel trusses. On the second-story level there was a wide quarter-mile running track along the inside walls. Today the track was filled with tables, chairs, and men in white jackets. This was where the physicals were taking place.

We were herded to an area on the lower level where everyone was handed a large paper bag. The people in charge of the bags shouted directions.

"Strip down. Take *everything* off and put it in the bag. Keep the bag and the paperwork with you at all times."

I had always felt uneasy about being nude in front of other guys—skinny-dipping in the Michigamme River—showering after a high school basketball game. But this—this was nudity on a grand scale. In a building half the size of the city of Ann Arbor I was stripping down in front of a thousand complete strangers. I gripped the medical questionnaire and paper bag with a clammy hand and barefooted my way up the iron staircase to the running track.

There weren't any kindly, gray-haired doctors. The running track was filled with white-coated "boy-doctors"—peach-fuzz-faced interns and students from the University Hospital and medical school—not much older than I was.

The first one snatched the medical questionnaire out of my hand and inspected it. "You didn't fill this out correctly," he snapped. "You put down that you've never received a vaccination or inoculation of any type."

"Uh... that's right," I replied. My parents didn't believe in medicine that had to be jabbed in with sharp instruments.

"No smallpox vaccination... diphtheria... tetanus... nothing?"

"Nuthin'."

He called to one of his coworkers. "Brad, we gotta virgin here... never been stuck."

Another boy-doctor eagerly came running up with a fistful of needles. Arm throbbing, I proceeded onward.

The morning wore on. My body was rudely violated with wooden sticks, tiny flashlights, and rubber-coated fingers. Surly boy-doctors looked into my eyes, scalp, and between my toes. Someone bashed my knee with a rubber mallet. My testicles were massaged. Indignity was heaped upon indignity.

I looked up at the track ahead, hoping to spot some relief, but all I could see were bare buttocks stretching off into infinity.

At long last, I made a complete circle of the running track and came to the staircase again. I eagerly padded down the stairs with my bag of clothes.

Successfully enduring the physical exam had boosted my appetite, and I rushed over to the West-Quad dining room for lunch. Today they were featuring creamed chipped beef on toast—commonly referred to by veteran West Quadders as SOS. To me, it tasted no worse than food at deer-hunting camp. I enthusiastically wolfed down the SOS and went up to my room to pour over my girl-script before the afternoon orientation.

At the two o'clock mixer everyone frantically bolted over to the group of girls. Even the most mild-mannered of us now realized there was only a split-second's difference between talking to a beauty queen and some plain-Jane also-ran.

By the time I got to the girls' table I found the pickings pretty lean, but no matter. I needed the opportunity to work the kinks out of my script, and it would be easier with a less-demanding subject.

I moved in on a skinny girl with heavy, horn-rimmed glasses.

"I seen you before," I stated flatly. "You were one'a the finalists in th'Marquette County Fair Beauty Contest last fall."

She quickly took off her glasses and began massaging the imprints from the bridge of her nose. Buttram was right; you could dish out any amount of outrageous flattery to a plain-looking girl and she'd swallow it hook, line, and sinker.

"Aha! It *was* you," I cried, adlibbing masterfully. "I wuz right, now that I see you without your glasses."

She shook her head reluctantly and gave me a timid smile, while furiously finger-combing her hair. "No... it wasn't me. I'm from Grand Rapids. I don't even know where Marquette County is."

"It's in Upper Michigan... tha's where I'm from." I introduced myself. "You must have a long-lost twin sister up there, heh, heh, heh."

It was an excellent start, but I had to move along since I had a lengthy agenda. "Would you like somethin'? The coffee here is purty good." I had learned not to give them refreshment choices—too expensive and time-consuming.

I brought the coffee over and went through my list of bright quips and probing questions that I'd organized the night before. Just before the half-hour was up I whipped out a slip of paper and a fountain pen and slid them in front of her. "If you don' mind puttin' down yer name an' telephone number, I thought we mebbe could get together sum night an' I could tell you more 'bout Upper Michigan."

She smiled again, nodded her head, and put down her name and number. I said goodbye and strode confidently over to the door, just in time to join Radcliff and the rest of the group.

Wednesday, September 19th, 1951
Waterman Gym

Radcliff marched us back over to Waterman Gym today, this time to register for classes. Overnight, the decor had been transformed from an army of nude bodies to a vast thicket of white signs advertising every conceivable academic course known to Western man. Signs were hanging from the railing around the running track and projecting up from the basketball courts. Beneath each sign was a makeshift table—sawhorses and a sheet of plywood—manned by stone-faced, uncompromising faculty members.

Confusion reigned. Students were running in all directions, loudly cursing the various inequities imposed on them by the system.

Each of us clutched a long perforated form known as the Railroad Ticket, made up of a dozen perforated sections requiring identical personal information. One section was torn off for each registered class.

Without Radcliff we would have been totally lost, but he expertly steered us over to the "Freshman Engineering" tables.

I was shuttled into one of the long lines and finally got up to the table, setting my paperwork down in front of a sullen-looking engineering professor chomping on an unlit cigar butt.

Last night I had diligently poured over the engineering catalog, crafting an ideal class schedule. This schedule didn't have a single class until ten o'clock each morning. I held it out to the man.

"Here's the courses'n times I'd like t'have, sir," I volunteered, thinking that I would save him a lot of time.

The professor wasn't even listening. He was peering at my high school transcript, wrinkling his nose as though he smelled something bad. He began to scribble furiously on several sections of my Railroad Ticket. "Can you handle two math courses this semester?"

"Two?" I said. "Don' I just take Math 13? Th'algebra and anlitik geometry?"

He didn't even look up as he continued to write. "How can you take analytic geometry when you haven't even had solid geometry or trigonometry yet? You're deficient in math, don't you know that? You should have had trigonometry and solid geometry in high school. You're going to have to take these courses—at no credit this semester—just to satisfy the entrance requirements. We call them 'dumbbell math.' If you pass them, you can take Math 13 next spring."

He paused and put a match to his cigar butt. "I'm surprised you even got *accepted* into engineering. Must have been that Regents Alumni Scholarship deal you fell into." He shook his head with disbelief, wondering how someone so deficient in mathematics could actually qualify for four years of free tuition. Finally, he finished writing, tore off a series of sections from my Railroad Ticket, and slapped a class schedule down on the plywood. "Here's your schedule of classes."

I picked it up and stared at it. An eight-o'clock class *every morning!* "Uh... sir, can't we switch this English 11 class at eight o'clock to th'one at ten?"

He smiled as though this was the dumbest question he had heard all morning. "Ten? That ten-o'clock class was filled up five minutes after we opened this morning." He took a final puff on his cigar, signalling that he was through with me. "Look, nobody wants five eight-o'clock classes, but *somebody's* got to take them. Besides, freshmen are *supposed* to suffer a little... builds character."

Five eight-o'clock classes and two math classes for no credit—not exactly an auspicious beginning—but my spirits lifted at the mid-morning mixer break. While I had successfully tested the validity of Buttram's scripted approach yesterday, today I had to work on timing.

Covertly maneuvering to the front of our group as we went through the League-cafeteria door, I quickly snagged a good-looking blonde. Cutting out some of my less-exciting dialogue, as well as questions that might require long, complicated answers, I had her name and phone number in less than fifteen minutes. Spotting a lone brunette who had already bought her own coffee—a lucky break—I bid the blonde an abrupt goodbye and moved over to the brunette's table. By the time the half-hour was up I also had her name and number. *Two girls in thirty minutes.* At this rate, I might easily corner the market on freshmen women.

Radcliff had given us Wednesday afternoon off to buy our supplies. Arms laden with textbooks, notebooks, and assorted drafting equipment (plastic triangles, French curves, and an unwieldy, four-foot T-square), I elbowed my way through the milling mob of students in Slater's Bookstore.

It didn't take long to run up a hefty bill, and I still had to buy the most expensive item—the slide rule. I didn't know a damn thing about slide rules except that I was going to need one.

Slater's had their own expert presiding over a slide-rule display case in the rear of the store.

Something in a slide rule, young man?" he asked.

"I guess so."

"Did you have a particular model in mind?" He knew from the pucker of my brow that I was going to have to be led by the hand through the entire transaction.

"How about a Post Versalog?" I asked, remembering the name of the slide rule that my roommate had shown me.

His eyes widened with respect. "Post Versalog? An excellent choice—the Cadillac of slide rules!" He reached into the display case and brought out a slide rule identical to the one that Rosenkranz had.

"I see that you're already familiar with an excellent engineering tool," he said, swiftly positioning and repositioning the middle strip and sliding glass window as he spoke, demonstrating how effortless it was to whip off complex calculations.

"I personally like the folded square-root scale for even and odd powers of ten," he said.

"Yeah," I replied vaguely.

"And for lightning-quick calculations of multiples of pi, you have the CF scale," he added.

"That'll come in handy," I said, warming up to the conversation.

"But then, of course," he exclaimed, his voice rising with enthusiasm, "you have the feature for which this instrument excels... scales for a range of natural logarithms from ten, to ten to the minus three." Eyes gleaming, he leaned toward me with an air of confidentiality. *Plus their reciprocals,* " he added with a note of triumph.

"Tha's pretty neat." I said.

"Shall I ring this up?" he asked.

"How much does it cost?"

"Twenty-six fifty."

I looked down into the display case and spotted a slide rule that had fewer numbers on it. "How much is that one?"

His expression changed. "You mean that... that... *aluminum* one?"

I nodded.

"Eight seventy-five," he sneered.

"I'll take it."

Thursday, September 20th, 1951
The Michigan League

Following an early-morning tour of the Intramural Sports Building and the football stadium, our orientation group hiked back up to the League for our ten-o'clock mixer break, arriving a few minutes early. I had already snagged a table when I saw *her* at the door.

She was wearing a baby blue cashmere sweater that radiated its own light, bathing her in a soft glow. Shoulder-length, Rita Hayworth-like reddish-brown hair and large, hazel eyes fringed with thick, dark lashes.

The more-experienced white-bucks in our group also spotted her, and sucking in a collective hot breath, they made a beeline for her.

A few short days ago I wouldn't, in my wildest dreams, have approached such a woman, but competition breeds guts. Struggling for traction on the tile floor, I outlegged the other pursuers and motioned her to my table.

"I've seen you before," I purred, launching into my now-well-polished opening salvo as I held her chair. "You were one of the finalists in the Marquette County Fair Beauty Contest last fall, weren't you?"

Obviously accustomed to such wanton flattery, she simply smiled and shook her head, waiting for me to continue. I silently congratulated myself for having the foresight to write the script. Now, it was paying off big. The names and numbers of the other girls could be discarded—mere pawns in rehearsal for the real thing—*the girl of my dreams.*

I quickly produced two cups of coffee and loosened her up with brave tales of my early years in the Upper Peninsula—hunting the mighty deer, trapping ferocious muskrat, and catching elusive brook trout.

I spent the entire half-hour with her—there was no need to talk to others. At a quarter past the hour it was time to switch the discussion to my career plans. I explained that I was going to become an aerodynamicist (I'd looked the word up the night before) and specialize in the design of supersonic (I'd also looked *that* up) aircraft. I offered to explain the theory of supersonic flight to her. My bluff paid off—she declined, laughingly claiming that she wouldn't understand a word of it. I carefully inserted questions here and there as Buttram had instructed and paid rapt attention to her answers.

Her name was Bernice. She was from Flint and intended to major in literature. She had never been to the Upper Peninsula and thought that my stories were fascinating—especially told with my "cute" accent. Would I tell her more about the place?

"We're almost out of time," I explained, whipping out my brand-new pocket address book with one hand and producing a fountain pen with the other, "but why don't we get together this weekend?"

Then, I had an even better idea. "Tomorrow, th'freshmen have to pick up their season football tickets at Waterman. Why don' we go together and get seats next to each other?"

Her eyes sparkled, and she clapped her hands in delight. "Oooh, that would be wonderful." She lightly touched my hand, sending shivers of delight through my body.

That night, I extended my girl-script to cover our date on Friday.

Friday, September 21st, 1951
Waterman Gym

Bright and early Friday morning Bernice and I met at Waterman and picked up our complimentary football tickets.

Being lowly freshmen, we were issued the worst seats in the stadium—high up in the end zone—miles from the gridiron. I didn't mind. I knew nothing about football anyway, since Republic High School was too small to have a team. The important thing was that I would be sitting next to Bernice at every home game.

The last orientation for freshmen engineering students was held that afternoon. We gathered in one-hour shifts in a large assembly room in the West Engineering building. A tall, hawk-nosed engineering professor spoke to us. He meandered around a variety of mundane topics relating to the College of Engineering, but his final remarks got everyone's attention.

"Each of you look at the person to your left and then the one to your right," he said. We did as we were instructed. "Next year at this time," he continued, "one of those people won't be here."

No one uttered a word—most not grasping the significance of what he had said.

"Past experience has shown that approximately one-third of you freshmen will be unable to cope with the pace of the classes, the depth of the material, and the technical demands placed upon you by your professors. These students will either be failed or will elect to leave before the year is out. The College of Engineering faculty is so certain of this that we only have the resources to accommodate two-thirds of you as sophomores. Needless to say, it behooves you to give it your very best effort. The competition will be very stiff. Good luck." With a motion of his hand, he dismissed us.

Walking out, I recalled that in high school I'd known kids just like the ones he was talking about—didn't do the work or just couldn't hack it. I was glad that I'd never had trouble with schoolwork.

During the past week I had decided on a prudent course of action. I would endure *one* semester just to show my mother and the old man that I could do it and that it wasn't particularly difficult. But once they started getting bills for the dormitory fees and other expenses, I wouldn't have much trouble convincing them that a steady tool-and-die maker paycheck made more sense than four years of college. Then, I'd pack up for Milwaukee and start shopping around for a new Buick—one of those fancy ones with an automatic dynaflow transmission.

Monday, October 1st, 1951
East Hall

At eight a.m. I merged with the herd of freshmen engineers thundering up the stairs in East Hall. The old wooden staircase squeaked and shook in protest. Rumor had it that East Hall had been proposed for condemnation before the Depression. The entire building actually shuddered every hour on the hour when battalions of engineering students arrived and departed for classes.

Today was the beginning of the second week of fall-semester classes. I edged into the English 11 room and took a seat at the rear as Professor Eli Stern began passing back our graded theme blue books. Last Monday, in our very first class, he had assigned a three-hundred-word theme—due last Friday—on the type of engineering career we intended to pursue.

When Stern handed me my blue book I was afraid to open it since I hadn't known what I was doing when I wrote it. I had an uneasy feeling about that theme. My high school English classes had concentrated on the rules of punctuation, the art of etching out convoluted sentence diagrams, and a few literary classics deemed to be proper reading for young minds. I didn't actually *write* much of anything. How bad could the grade be? I wondered—a B-minus?—more likely a C.

Finally summoning up the nerve to peek inside the cover, I was jarred by the gigantic red *D-minus*. There had to be some mistake. I had *never* gotten a D in high school.

But obviously, Stern didn't care much for my effort. Irate red-ink comments ran all over the pages. In fact, there was now more red ink than black on my theme.

Gazing in annoyance at his scruffy band of greenhorns, Stern rapped his desk impatiently with a ruler, silencing the room. "I was dismayed to see the incredibly inept level of writing skill that some of you displayed on this first assignment. In fact, the average grade was only a C-plus."

He shook his head slowly to further emphasize his disapproval. "Ordinarily, I don't tolerate such underachievement in my classes, especially with a subject as simple as describing your engineering career goals."

As a tenured professor in the English Department, Stern had little use for engineers, vastly preferring to instruct those who had chosen the more refined fields of literature and the arts.

With a thin, frosty smile, he added, "However, I tend to be somewhat lenient during the first week of classes. From now on I expect to see significant improvement."

His expression became grim. "For those of you who received a grade lower than a C, I recommend that you seek immediate help."

Stern erased the blackboard, indicating that the first theme was now water under the bridge and that we were starting afresh this morning. He wrote "Technology Challenges for the Engineer in the Year 1951" on the blackboard.

"Your next assignment is a four-hundred-word theme on this subject—due on Friday, of course." He extracted notes from his briefcase and straightaway launched into a mind-numbing lecture on the transition of focus across paragraphs.

Four hundred words! Do these things grow in size every week? Crissakes—by the end of the semester we'll be cranking out whole books between Monday and Friday!

I quickly copied the assignment from the blackboard. What the hell are technology challenges, I wondered, not realizing that I was in the midst of one.

At the end of the lecture I cautiously approached Stern. "Ahhh... sir, I'm comin' t'you, like y'said, t'get sum help."

He snatched the blue book from my hand, read my name on the cover and briefly glanced at the D-minus and the red-ink comments on the inside pages. He handed it back, glaring at me over his reading glasses.

"Mr. Harju," he said icily. "When I spoke of seeking immediate help, I did not mean that you should seek it from *me*. Aside from the editorial comments I place in the blue books, I do not have the time to provide personal guidance to engineering students with inadequate English backgrounds. You must seek this tutelage on your own. However, there are many talented upperclassmen in the English Department who will be more than happy to provide this service... for a fee, of course."

He impatiently whipped out a gold Bulova pocket watch from a vest pocket—signalling that our conversation had ended—and walked out of the room.

Already late for my engineering-drawing class, I had to hurry out too.

The shabby engineering-drawing classroom was nestled in the attic of the West Engineering building. I quickly taped last-week's masterpiece—a plan-view pencil-drawing of an I-beam—onto the drafting table as Professor Ed Smutch spoke to the class.

Smutch and Stern had a common desire to weed out the dull-brained and weak-willed freshmen to make room for the surviving sophomores-to-be, but otherwise they were a study in contrasts. Stern, always nattily attired in a freshly pressed suit, absolutely hated coming over to the dingy, run-down engineering buildings to teach. On the other hand, Smutch, a professor in the Mechanical Engineering Department, was an *engineer's* engineer. He must have had other jobs besides teaching drafting—perhaps disembowelling large machines—because his hands were permanently grease-etched. His clothes were severely rumpled, and an ancient necktie displayed remnants of past lunches. A chain smoker, he liberally polluted the classroom with cigarette smoke. From time to time, while he was inspecting classwork in progress, Smutch's cigarette would drop a live coal on the drawing paper, forcing the student to extinguish it quickly to keep his precious work from going up in flames.

"Last week was child's play," Smutch rumbled ominously, referring to the I-beam drawing that we had slaved over for three class periods. "Today will be different. Get out your India ink and pens. We're going to transfer that I-beam to ink on vellum."

He handed out 24"x36" sheets of vellum—a semitransparent, glossy paper used for making blueprint masters—and gave us instructions on using pen and ink. We mounted the vellum over the pencilled I-beam drawing and very carefully loaded our pens with India ink.

"Be careful with that ink," Smutch advised. "If you spill it on your clothes, there's only one way to remove it... a razor blade."

The object of the morning's class was to trace our original pencil-drawing of the I-beam onto the overlaid vellum. It sounded easy. In reality, it was much more difficult than drawing the original because of the cantankerous nature of capillary-action pens. If your mind wandered or your hand twitched ever so slightly, the pen had a nasty habit of urinating a blob of ink onto your paper.

But of course I didn't know that this Monday morning as I began tracing the line-work onto the vellum. As the two-hour period drew to a close, I was almost finished. The inked vellum transfer was beautiful—every line straight and true, every letter and number perfectly formed. Suddenly my vision became obscured by smoke. Smutch was leaning over my shoulder.

"That's a fine piece of work there, young Harju," Smutch said pleasantly. "Yessir... worthy of an A."

An A! My right hand began to tremble violently and twisted into a spastic knot. Sensing this, the pen maliciously spit out a puddle of ink the size of Lake Superior. It trickled gleefully across the I-beam drawing, down to the bottom of the sheet, over the edge of the drafting table and dripped onto my right pant leg.

"Oh, my, my... would you look at that!" Smutch exclaimed, feigning alarm. "It would appear that you'll have to start over. Well, it just so happens that this room won't be used again until one o'clock. If you work quickly through lunch, I'm sure you can produce another vellum almost as good as this one would have been. That is, if you're more careful."

Chuckling to himself, he ambled off in a cloud of cigarette smoke to torture the poor wretch at the next table.

I redid the I-beam vellum during the lunch hour and hustled over to my one-o'clock chemistry class, glumly taking stock of my scholastic predicament. Things were grim. The remainder of my first-semester load (chemistry and the two "dumbbell math" courses—solid geometry and trigonometry) was as brutal as English and drafting.

Chemistry, like cooking, was a black art—practiced only by sorcerers and housewives, respectively. Even in high school, I'd had no concept of what made chemicals tick, and the chemistry taught at Michigan was strictly fast track.

I had a better grasp of math but the homework was staggering. Each night I sweated out grisly computations of cone frustum volumes, tangents of obtuse angles, and other murky enigmas, of interest *only* to the Einsteins of the universe. I was now on intimate terms with my new aluminum slide rule.

Throughout grade school and high school—with little or no effort—I'd been at or near the top of my class. But after one week of classes at Michigan, one thing was certain: I was nowhere *near* the top of the Engineering Class of '55. In fact, I was in imminent danger of becoming one of the casualties that the hawk-nosed professor had referred to at the close of Orientation Week.

It was ironic. Only two weeks ago I wanted to leave Michigan, and now I found myself fighting like hell to hang on.

Wednesday, November 7th, 1951
Allen Rumsey House

Promptly at nine p.m. I closed my solid geometry text, put away my slide rule, stood up from my desk, and stretched the kinks out of my back.

By now—the semester's seventh week—my life was total misery. I endured classes run by ruthless professors, wolfed down unidentifiable substances in the West-Quad dining room, groped with riddling mathematical equations and chemical formulae into the wee hours, and passed out on a lumpy mattress in a narrow iron bunk. I was up to my chin in a deep sea of feces, and each test or homework assignment was a wave. I was dogpaddling to stay alive.

As the fall semester dragged on through its dog days, anything in the dorm that even remotely resembled recreation was desperately embraced, no matter how primitive, uncivilized, or disgusting. The nine p.m. technical interchange meetings in room 301, the residence of one J. R. Moon, met this criteria.

J. R. Moon was a junior in mechanical engineering and was regarded by technical types in Allen Rumsey as a certifiable genius. He found studying an unnecessary bore, and his room was always open to lively discussions on all manner of subjects.

The format was always the same. A mid-evening crowd, seeking refuge from the books, would gather in room 301. J. R. would usually open the discussion with some outrageous statement, seemingly contrary to the laws of the universe. Puppy engineers and physicists in the room would rise to the bait and money usually changed hands. The discussion normally terminated with some type of field test—the most interesting portion of the evening.

The previous night, when a sufficient number had gathered, J. R. flatly stated that a prophylactic would hold three gallons of water without breaking.

"Not a chance," cried the group. Someone produced a prophylactic. A chemical engineer scrounged a beaker from his room. A slide rule was produced to compute the number of liters in three gallons. Coins and even a few dollar bills were tossed on J. R.'s bed and the experiment began.

We all trooped down to the bathroom at the end of the hall. J. R. proceeded to fill the prophylactic with water while someone logged the number of beakers of water.

Sure enough, three gallons were poured in and the prophylactic was still intact. J. R. chuckled triumphantly.

But we were not fulfilled. The exuberance, characteristic of J. R. Moon field tests, was missing. The group thought that there had to be some useful application for the loaded prophylactic. After tying off the opening, we lugged it back to room 301—not an easy task since three gallons of water gave the prophylactic the inertial properties of a pregnant octopus.

As luck would have it, J. R.'s window was located directly above the front door of Allen Rumsey. We spotted Oliver Stutz, a fat, pre-law freshman, waddling up the sidewalk, returning from his nightly journey to the Washtenaw Dairy. Stutz was carrying a cardboard holder filled with vanilla ice cream cones for himself and his roommate.

By now I had been indoctrinated in the intense animosity—dating back to the nineteenth century—between engineers and lawyers at Michigan. What could be more satisfying than dropping the loaded prophylactic on a lawyer's ice cream cones?

With the speed of a skilled artillery commander, J. R. estimated Stutz's walking velocity, computed the prophylactic's drop-time, and determined the precise instant for launch. Timing was critical—a slight miscalculation could result in hitting Stutz on the head, with possibly lethal results. With my long arms, I was selected as a member of the launch team.

"Launch!" J. R. cried as Stutz neared the entrance. Three of us pushed the prophylactic out the window. The trajectory was perfect. The prophylactic water bomb cleanly plucked the cone holder out of Stutz's hands, hammering vanilla ice cream into the pavement—another J. R. Moon project successfully carried to completion.

Tonight's technical topic had already been selected when I arrived in room 301.

"You're kidding," cried Murray Rosenkranz, my roommate. "You can't *burn* farts!"

"What do you think they're composed of?" J. R. said quietly. "Mostly methane. Methane is indeed very flammable."

I immediately sided with Rosenkranz. If farts were flammable, my old man would have blown our family to kingdom come every time he stood up from the dinner table and lit a cigarette.

"It's very easy to prove," J. R. continued. "All we need is a volunteer."

All eyes turned to Bubba Tibodeaux, a freshman from Lake Charles, Louisiana. Bubba was the undisputed third-floor farting champion—able to let one rip on command at any given moment. On the nights when the West-Quad dining room served franks and beans he was truly awesome.

"Ah kin let one pop fer ya, but it ain't gonna burn," Bubba stated flatly, showcasing his expertise on the subject.

J. R. produced a wooden match. "Drop your pants and shorts Bubba, and bend over."

Bubba looked dubious as he unbuckled his belt. "J. R., if you burn me with thet match..."

"Don't worry, the flame won't be that close to your skin."

Money came out. Bubba bet J. R. a dollar. I dug out a fifty-cent piece, also betting against J. R.

Bubba bent over, his bare butt gleaming in the light from J. R.'s gooseneck desk lamp.

J. R. lit the match. "You ready?"

"On the count of three," Bubba grunted from his hunched-over position. "One... two..."

J. R. quickly put the flaming match into position, about three inches from Bubba's backside.

"Three!" Bubba cried, letting a humongous one fly.

A wicked, bright blue flame—about five inches in length—shot out from Bubba. His rear end looked like the tailpipe of a F-86 Sabre Jet.

In fact, Bubba took off like an F-86. He bounded across the room, knocking over chairs and other objects in his path. The stench of burning hair hung heavily in the air.

"OW-OW-OW-OW! J. R., ah'm gonna kill yew! Y'burnt me with thet match."

J. R. scooped up the money from his blanket. "It wasn't the match, Bubba. Tell him, boys."

Thus mentally refreshed, I strolled back to my room, ready for another four-or-five-hour wrestling match with mathematics, chemistry, and English composition.

I passed Nathan McCool, resident of room 304, standing in his doorway. McCool gave me a withering look as he rolled a toothpick around in his mouth.

"I heard the laughing. What was it tonight? Dropping more rubber bombs on lawyers?"

McCool was a senior in business administration and, as such, was not invited to the nightly shenanigans in J. R. Moon's room—nor was he interested. Anything that went on in room 301 was light-years beneath him.

I couldn't help chuckling as I described the flammability test.

Unsmiling, McCool shook his head in disbelief. "I've seen you guys troop into Moon's room every night this semester... even weekends. Has your whole social life regressed to setting fire to farts? When's the last time you had a date with a girl?"

The question quickly punctured my good mood. The romance with Bernice from Flint had died a slow, agonizing death weeks ago.

Our first encounter during Orientation Week had set the pace. From then on, every time I opened my mouth she expected me to whip off scintillating bons mots. Swamped with homework and with no time to prepare my dialog, I soon clammed up like a wooden Indian. With her looks, Bernice never needed a reason to develop conversational skills, and at the first Michigan home football game we spent three excruciatingly silent hours together. After that she kept inventing excuses for not going to the rest of the games. I never saw her again.

"It's been awhile," I admitted morosely.

McCool's demeanor quickly changed. He gave me a slow, easy smile. "Want to take out a nice girl this Saturday?"

Nathan McCool was known in the Allen Rumsey dorm as "the fixer." He had contacts in every women's dormitory on campus and at a moment's notice could fix you up with a date. No one knew exactly why he did it. One opinion ventured was that he was serving a self-apprenticeship, and as soon as he got his B.A., he was going to move to the East Coast and start up a high-priced escort service. McCool had already contacted all of the freshmen in Allen Rumsey about getting them dates. Up to my ears in homework and still smarting from the disaster with Bernice, I'd turned him down.

"Well?" McCool asked.

"Ahhh... I don' think so," I replied timidly. "I gotta big English theme t'turn in on Monday mornin'... a chemistry blue book on Tuesday..."

McCool's eyes darted up and down the hallway, then leaned closer to indicate that what he was about to say was in strictest confidence. "I can fix you up with a *sorority* girl," he whispered.

My pulse blipped. How could that be? Only fraternity men took out sorority women. Dormitory men took out dormitory women. It was a well-understood caste system that was rarely violated. On the other hand, it would be a tremendous boost to my image—to say nothing of my ego—if word got around Allen Rumsey that I had a date with a sorority woman.

McCool caught the spark of interest in my eyes and pressed on. "You're kind of a shy guy around women, am I right? Well, the girl I've got in mind is a good match for you—an excellent conversationalist and doesn't mind the strong silent type. All you have to do is nod your head and smile."

Saturday, November 10th, 1951
Allen Rumsey House

At six-thirty p.m. I stood in front of the wall mirror in my room nervously preparing for the blind date that McCool had arranged.

Dick Beaudry, my next door neighbor in room 311, looked at me incredulously from the doorway. "A necktie with airplanes flying across it?"

"They're B-17 bombers," I replied as I finished putting the knot in my prized possession, a necktie with a formation of B-17 Flying Fortresses in flight across the sky blue, six-inch-wide rayon material.

"Is that the only tie you have?"

"No, but it's th'best one."

"At least put a Windsor knot in it," Beaudry advised. Beaudry came from Grosse Pointe, a posh Detroit suburb, and had become the third-floor de facto advisor on wardrobe and cultural matters.

"What'za Winser knot?"

"Ah... never mind. Actually, that knot you made goes rather well with the tie. So, where are you taking this sorority girl?"

"There's a brand-new Gary Cooper movie at the State Theater... *Distant Drums*."

Beaudry's jaw dropped. "You're taking a sorority girl to a *cowboys and Indians* movie?"

"No good, huh? Whut else is there?" I asked.

"For one thing, *The Seagull* is playing at the Lydia Mendelssohn Theater in the League building."

"*The Seagull?*"

"Yes. The comedy by Anton Chekhov."

"A comedy?" I exclaimed, putting on my suit coat. "I like comedies. I ain' seen a good funny movie since I left home."

"This isn't a movie," Beaudry said. "It's a four-act play."

"Oh, yeah? The only play I ever seen wuz one I had a part in. Our junior class at Republic High School put it on... pretty funny, too."

"Yes... well... a word of caution." Beaudry said, eyeing me carefully and speaking slowly. "If you go to *The Seagull*, don't laugh unless you hear the rest of the audience laughing."

A chilly evening wind whipped through the large trees overhanging Washtenaw Avenue as I hurried over to the Delta Tau sorority house.

At the last minute, I'd pulled out my girl-script used so successfully during Orientation Week and refreshed my memory on the clever dialog. If she was as good a talker as McCool claimed, there was easily enough conversational material to get me through the evening—especially if we were watching a play.

Three-story white columns guarded the tall, oak front door of the Delta Tau sorority house. It was a huge, brick colonial-style mansion set well back from the street. I knocked on the door, bruising my knuckles on the thick wood. Then I noticed the doorbell and rang it. A muted chime ding-donged off in the distance.

The door sighed reluctantly as it opened. A pretty girl smiled politely at me. "Who is it you wish to see?"

My mind went blank. I hastily dug the piece of paper out of my pants pocket. "Eleanor Ridgerock," I said.

She opened the door wider, momentarily glancing at my necktie. "Come in, please."

The foyer was as large as the whole first floor of our house in Upper Michigan. A wide, richly varnished wooden staircase curved gracefully up to a spacious second-floor landing. A magnificent crystal chandelier, the size of a Chevrolet, reached down from the soaring ceiling, casting soft light on Persian rugs artfully positioned on the hardwood floor. Imperious-looking middle-aged women—influential alumnae of Delta Tau, no doubt—stared disapprovingly at me from dark oil paintings on the walls.

The girl who let me in pressed one of several buttons on a wall-mounted panel. "Won't you take a seat?" she said. "Eleanor will be down shortly." I sat down gingerly on an antique chair upholstered in a heavy brocade.

Two fraternity-type fellows entered without ringing the doorbell. They punched buttons on the panel with practiced familiarity and sat down next to me. Each wore a navy blue sports coat, gray flannel slacks, and white-buck shoes. They stared at my tie.

The B-17 engines on my necktie turned over with a whine and roared to life. The Delta Tau foyer began filling up with deafening noise and aviation-fuel exhaust.

Several girls passed through the foyer—all beautiful and exquisitely dressed. My blind date was certain to be a doll. Would my mind freeze up like it did on the last date with Bernice? With effort, I got a grip on myself, reasoning that after all, with the girl-script fresh in my mind, I should handle the situation easily.

Footsteps on the staircase echoed in the foyer. I looked up, froze, and blinked my eyes several times. A bear was coming down the stairs—in high heels. The bear came up to me, stopped, and looked me up and down, eyes pausing briefly on my necktie.

"Hi, I'm Eleanor."

She was a very large girl wearing a full-length, dark brown mink coat. She towered over me by several inches, and judging from the width of her shoulders, she probably outweighed me by at least thirty pounds—maybe more, it was hard to tell with the fur coat. I scrambled out of the chair and stood up.

Looking down critically at the top of my head, she said, "Just a minute. I'll be right back." She clacked back up the stairs in her heels and moments later padded down, somewhat shorter now in dark blue tennis shoes. She was still about six-one.

Eleanor had nice, even features—lean square jaw, long straight nose, and piercing blue eyes—fairly attractive if she had been a man. This woman could easily have passed for John Wayne's twin sister.

I squeaked out my name as she grabbed my hand, turning it to instant hamburger with a bone-crushing shake. The girl-script was useless. There was no way I could look her in the eye with a straight face and say that I thought she was one of the finalists in the Marquette County Fair Beauty Contest. The Marquette County Fair Log-Splitting Contest, maybe.

"Excuse the shoes," she said. "Our sorority date coordinator always tries to line me up with guys at least six-four. I guess your dorm contact didn't get the word."

I shook my head, making a mental note to set Nathan McCool's hair on fire.

"So where're we headed?" Eleanor asked as we walked down the sidewalk.

*She was a very large girl wearing a full length,
dark brown mink coat.*

"There's a play at the Lydia Mendelssohn. *The Seagull*."

"Oh, yes... by Chekhov," she replied enthusiastically. "I'm a contemporary-literature major. I'm glad you picked *The Seagull*. It's a favorite of mine. I hope they have a believable cast tonight. I saw an off-Broadway version of it last year, and would you believe that the fellow who played Constantine Gavrilovich Treplev had a *New York accent?* He sounded like a cab driver." She chuckled at the absurdity of it all.

McCool had been right about one thing. She was a strong conversationalist. The only trouble was I didn't know what the hell she was conversing about. Should I try to fake it? No—I was too ignorant to try anything devious.

I said, "This... Constantine Gavri... Gavri... whatever his name is. He almost sounds like a Russian or somethin'."

There was a short silence. "Yes... Russian. The whole play takes place in Russia," she replied in measured tones. "In fact, *all* of Chekhov's plays take place in Russia."

"Oh, I see... tha's great. Are there spies in it?"

Eleanor half-snorted as she tried to suppress a laugh. "Spies, that's good. There aren't any spies in Chekhov's plays. You see, they all take place around the turn of the century... before the Russian revolution." She paused. "You're not familiar with Chekhov's plays at all, are you?"

"I never been to a play in my life, except one we put on in high school," I said truthfully.

She was astonished. "You've *never* seen a play?"

I shook my head.

She stared at the sidewalk intently. "Oh... well... I suppose you read novels though, right?"

I smiled and nodded enthusiastically. A copy of Mickey Spillane's *I, The Jury* had just completed the rounds on the third floor of Allen Rumsey, each guy gettin one hour to read the marked-up, steamy sections. "Yeah. I love novels."

She brightened up. "Have you read Tolstoy's works?"

"'Tolstoy's Works,'... I guess I missed that one."

"No... no... I meant novels written by Leo Tolstoy."

I shook my head again.

"How about Sinclair Lewis?" she asked.

"Ahhh... nope."

"Aldous Huxley... *Brave New World?*" she said hopefully.

"No."

Her face hardened with defeat. "You're an *engineer*, aren't you?"

"Yeah, tha's right. How'd ya know?"

The Seagull was *not* a comedy. In fact, it was a tragedy since I missed a brand-new Gary Cooper western because of it. For three hours, people with jaw-breaking names stood around onstage making stupid conversation. A couple of them were writers, serving to remind me that I still had my English 11 theme to do for Monday morning. The fourth act mercifully ground to a halt when the main character committed suicide. The only seagull in the play was dead, most likely dying from boredom.

But Eleanor enjoyed the play, and on the walk back to the sorority house, she carried on at some length about the unfulfilled love between Constantine Gavrilovich and Nina Mikhailovna and the symbolism of the seagull. I tagged along with a tight grin on my face, nodding from time to time. I didn't ask her what symbolism was; the seagull just looked plain dead to me.

At the Delta Tau doorway she smiled and I got another firm handshake. "I had a nice time tonight and really enjoyed the play. Thank you very much."

She looked at me appraisingly. "Can I give you some advice? Don't wind up like the rest of the engineers I've seen around campus who graduate after four years only knowing gear ratios and tensile strengths. Pick up some good literature and read. You might really like it." She turned and went inside.

I strode down Washtenaw Avenue deep in thought. Eleanor Ridgerock was right. As long as I was in college I ought to broaden myself. Use my nine p.m. breaks for reading—no more betting on bizarre experiments in room 301. First thing Monday morning I'd pop down to Slater's Bookstore and pick out something from the literature section to expand my mind.

It was getting late and I picked up the pace. The State Theater was having a midnight showing of *Distant Drums*.

Saturday, December 22nd, 1951
Mackinaw City, Michigan

The light in the late-afternoon overcast sky was fading rapidly as we approached Mackinaw City from the south. Snow flurries and long dark expanses of spruce trees were reminders that on the other side of the Straights of Mackinac was the Upper Peninsula. The Mackinac Bridge was still under construction, so we had to catch the Mackinaw City-St. Ignace ferry.

I was riding with Steve Maki in his '48 Chevy. Steve was also a freshman engineer living in Allen Rumsey. When I learned that he was from Marquette we quickly became friends, since neither of us knew anyone else at the university who was from the Upper Peninsula. Steve kept his car with a relative in Ypsilanti but frequently drove back and forth to Marquette on semester breaks, holidays, and long weekends.

I didn't know how he managed to get away that much. My academic struggles hadn't permitted the luxury of trips. This Christmas vacation was the first time I'd been out of Ann Arbor since the semester began.

I'd dealt with periodic bouts of homesickness, usually brought on by letters from home. My mother's letters were always chock-full of good advice—wear my galoshes—dress warmly—eat all the food served in the West-Quad dining room (I didn't consider *that* to be good advice).

But it was the short letters from the old man that truly touched me. His note of last month read:

> *Hello Jerry,*
>
> *Everything is OK here. We get a light snow every morning now. Good for tracking when deer season opens next week. I still go walking around in the cemetery every morning early and see the tracks of that old buck you didn't get three years ago. He still crosses through before sunup, right on schedule. Maybe you can get him next year if you get some time off from school in deer season.*
>
> *Pop*

The words weren't elegant, but my heart always ached for a time after reading them.

The three-month, self-imposed confinement at Michigan had paid off. I was eking out passing grades. Even without the benefit of a tutor, my theme-work in English 11 had improved enough so that I'd probably manage a C for a final grade. I'd do about the same in chemistry. Notwithstanding the harassment from Professor Smutch, I had a good handle on engineering-drawing and could pull an A. Unless I screwed up the final exams, I expected B's in solid geometry and trigonometry. My grade-point average was going to be lower than any I'd ever gotten in high school, but it appeared that I was actually going to make it through the first semester.

The College of Engineering had already taken its toll. Two freshmen engineers living on the third floor of Allen Rumsey had packed up their bags and slunk off for home. The student population in all of my classes had dwindled. Smart kids from large high schools were dropping like flies, but I still hung on. I was earning my stripes in a hellishly rigorous, demanding environment, and while I didn't admit it to anyone, I was proud.

The light was getting too dim to read, so I put my book away. Yesterday I'd bought Huxley's *Brave New World* and started on it this morning as we pulled out of Ann Arbor. I was almost finished.

Steve wanted to talk. "Whaddaya think of this car?"

"Your car? It's neat."

"Y'wanna buy it?"

That took me by surprise. "Y'selling it? Why?"

"Gonna get a new one."

"A new one... how you gonna afford that?"

Steve grinned guiltily. "Well... I ain't told nobody yet—not even my folks—but this semester is it for me. Grades aren't what they should be, and besides, I've got a surveying job lined up with the ol' Cleveland Cliff Iron Company, starting in February. They're lookin' for people with some math and drafting under their belt. Good pay, too. So... you wanna buy the Chevy or not?"

"I ain't got any money. Y'know that."

"Yeah, but you told me you're quitting school in February, too. Use the Chevy for awhile and trade it in on that new Buick you been talkin' about when you get down to Milwaukee."

I stared out at the snowflakes landing on the windshield. "I been thinking I'd stick it out for another semester."

Steve snorted. "After all that talk you gave me about not wanting four more years of cracking books with no money in your pockets... why?"

"I dunno," I said, rubbing my tired eyes. "I'm not sure I know the answer to *that* one myself."

Thursday, March 20th, 1952
West Engineering Building

Heinrich Stielhaus, our metallurgy professor, handed out safety goggles to everyone. "Nothing will happen when the test bar breaks—I assure you—but extra caution is always a good idea."

Right, I thought. If it's so safe, why the goggles? They probably concluded that it was a good idea after steel shards shot through the eye sockets and into the brain of some poor freshman engineering student.

Today's metallurgy lab was going to explore the tensile strength of molybdenum steel by using a tensile-test machine to pull apart a molybdenum test bar. Stielhaus had us clustered around the rhinoceros-sized machine while he fastened the test bar between its large jaws. He pressed a red button. Somewhere within the machine a hydraulic heart grunted to life, and the jaws began pulling on the test bar.

Everyone poised pencils over their notebooks. The student lab assignment was to record the readings from various gauges before the bar failed.

Stielhaus motioned for us to edge closer to the test bar. "I want you to observe the final plastic deformation of the test bar before it breaks."

There was frantic jockeying for position—not to get closer, but to maneuver other guys into the front row as a shield against flying shrapnel.

The tensile-test machine hummed, and the needles on the gauges crept upward. I was busily copying down readings—hard to do with sweaty hands.

BBBBBBAAAAAANNNNNNGGGGGG!!!!!!

Everyone flinched, dropping their pencils, as the huge machine pulled the molybdenum bar in two with a deafening report. Above the ringing in my ears I could hear Stielhaus saying, "Gentlemen, I hope you got those final numbers written down. We'll be discussing this test next week." I picked up my pencil from the floor.

After the lab I trudged back to the West Quad, dwelling on the foolishness of enrolling for the spring semester. I was not doing well at all in several courses.

Second-semester chemistry was supposed to be much tougher than the first course, so there weren't any surprises there. The only surprise would be if I passed it.

Theme writing in English 11 had been no picnic, but at least the extent of my stupidity had been kept between Professor Stern and myself. Now, in English 21—oral expression—I was forced to get up in front of the class and speak, allowing large numbers of people to observe my dumbness first hand. Every time I had to go on center stage I was paralyzed with fright as I faced my fellow freshmen—each one praying I would screw up, thereby lowering the grade curve.

But metallurgy was the worst. Concepts like polymorphism, crystallographic planes, coherent precipitates, and decalescence had to be memorized and understood. The nerve-jangling Thursday-afternoon lab was thrown in for good measure.

In the West Quad lobby, I found one letter in my mailbox—an official-looking envelope from the College of Engineering. This was unsettling—perhaps the dean was saving me the embarrassment of flunking the finals and advising me to leave right now. I opened the envelope.

To University of Michigan engineering students:

The United States Army is forming a student-cooperative program at the White Sands Proving Ground in New Mexico. The White Sands facility is currently being used for government rocket research.

The University of Michigan has been invited to participate in this program. Students in the cooperative program will work as government employees at White Sands during the fall and winter months and attend classes in Ann Arbor during the spring and summer.

Selected College of Engineering students will be given the opportunity to apply. If you are interested in the White Sands cooperative program, please make an appointment with the Assistant Dean's office as soon as possible. Enrollment will be limited.

Walter P. Emmert
Assistant Dean
College of Engineering
University of Michigan

I looked at the envelope again to make sure I hadn't received it by mistake. I reread the letter several times.

They're inviting *me* to sign up for this? New Mexico—jeezus—that's on the other side of the *Mississippi!* Testing rockets—*real* rockets—not models! As a kid, I had built a model of every plane used in World War II. I was in love with anything that flew. I *had* to get into that program.

I rushed to the nearest telephone and called Professor Emmert's office. The secretary said I was the first student to respond to the letter. She set up my appointment for the following week.

Later I was eating dinner in the dining room with a bunch of third-floor Allen Rumsey guys. Edward Goldfarb, our fish expert from Coos Bay, Oregon, delicately tasted the entree on his plate, the mysterious salmon patties that the West Quad served up frequently.

"No way in hell that's salmon," he stated categorically.

"Ah think it's fried-up stale bread soaked in cod-liver oil... thet's whut ah think," Bubba Tibodeaux said.

I was too excited about the White Sands letter to join into the usual high-spirited evening analysis of the West-Quad food. I splashed a liberal amount of catsup on the salmon patties to kill the taste.

"You guys get the White Sands letter from Emmert's office?" I asked.

"I got one," said Rosenkranz.

"You gonna apply?"

"You kiddin?" Rosenkranz retorted. "The U.S. rocket program is a joke! If I was gonna spend my time in a co-op program—which I'm not—I'd be designing jet planes. That's the way of the future. Forget rockets."

"Emmert is going to be picking guys with good grade-point averages for that program," added J. R. Moon. "You can bet on that."

Gawd, I thought, if Moon is right, I don't stand a chance of going to White Sands. Here I am, almost flunking three courses.

I downed the catsup-smothered salmon patties and hurried back to the room to attack my homework.

Professor Stielhaus had assigned a take-home metallurgy blue book to be completed and handed in at tomorrow's eight o'clock class. A take-home blue book—an exam done outside of class—sounded easy because you could take your time looking up the answers. But the questions were intricate and convoluted—much harder than class exams. The answers required incisive analysis and digging through reams of reference material. I sharpened a handful of pencils. This would be an all-night affair.

The warm weather didn't make the take-home blue book any easier. Today—the first day of spring—had dawned sunny and clear, polishing off the remaining soot-encrusted snowbanks along Ann Arbor curbs. Of course, Michigan weather never cooperated with the calendar; Mother Nature regularly served up one or two March or April blizzards just to keep Michiganders on their toes. But everyone was celebrating the glory of the moment, throwing windows open to air out dorm rooms that had endured long winter months of cigarette smoke and unwashed bodies.

The failed crop of freshmen engineers had left several vacancies in Allen Rumsey, and Bob Buttram had moved down the hall, leaving room 309 to Rosenkranz and me. I sat at my desk near the open window, bathed by warm breezes, trying hard to concentrate on a problem that posed the question: Why does the addition of thirty percent nickel to copper have less effect on electrical conductivity than the addition of five percent aluminum to copper?

Sam Bumford in room 319 began blowing his trumpet out of the open window. Bumford hadn't brought out the trumpet since the Homecoming football game last fall, but you could tell who it was. He always played the same thing—"Serenade in Blue"—and he always fell just a tad flat on the same high note.

His room and mine overlooked Madison Street and the South Quad, the new high-rise men's dorm across the street. In a matter of minutes, someone in the South Quad stuck a trombone through his open window and launched into a fractured version of "Hold That Tiger."

Volleys of "Knock it off" were fired from both dorms, but the two musicians continued to duel. Maynard Smythe, an Allen Rumsey classical-music aficionado, dragged a twelve-inch woofer over to his first-floor window and blasted Beethoven's fifth symphony out onto Madison Street. Some South Quad Neanderthal retaliated by aiming his speaker at the window, turning on a ten-thousand-watt amplifier and bathing the city of Ann Arbor with one-hundred-and-ninety decibels of "Cocktails for Two" by Spike Jones. A fog horn blared. Someone set off a string of firecrackers. All the nervous, frustrated energy pent up in stuffy little rooms over the winter exploded into the balmy air between the two quadrangles.

The noise was overwhelming, so I picked up my metallurgy books and papers to seek refuge in the nearby Michigan Union. Suddenly, I noticed guys from both dorms beginning to gather on the street. Intrigued by the prospect of witnessing a large-scale fistfight, I put my stuff down and watched.

A couple hundred West and South Quadders squared off on opposite curbs of Madison Street, sneering and taunting each other with miscellaneous threats. This went on for several minutes while the rest of us watched from open windows. But no one seemed inclined to get physical, and after a bit the confrontation began losing steam. I again picked up my books to go to the Union.

Then, two Ann Arbor police cars arrived.

The noise on the street and at the dorm windows became an ominous rumble. Someone put "Slaughter on Tenth Avenue" on his phonograph. Allen Rumsey house trembled as bodies charged down the stairs to get to the street. The squad cars drew people like moths to a light bulb. In less than a minute, the crowd swelled to over a thousand.

I headed for the door to join them when I remembered the metallurgy blue book. I had to pass this exam if I expected to get into the White Sands co-op program. I sat down again but continued to watch the action in the street.

With the growing size of the mob it was impossible to keep the West and South Quadders apart. Both factions flowed together in the middle of the street, hostilities between the two dorms now forgotten, replaced by one common purpose—harassing the police.

Guys completely enveloped the squad cars, rocking the vehicles so violently that the bumpers scraped the pavement, throwing off sparks. The cops sat inside, petrified.

I was mesmerized. The only mobs I had ever seen were in the movies—lynch mobs and prison riots. This was the real thing.

It was getting dark and flashlights flared in the crowd. One flashlight-holder screamed something above the din—I couldn't make it out—and the mass of students began to move—at first sluggishly but then with more resolve—down Madison toward State Street. The police put the squad cars in low gear and followed.

My door burst open. Some guy—I didn't even know his name—who lived down at the end of the hall yelled, "They're going to the women's dorms!"

"Why?" I asked.

"To invade 'em... what else?" he cried, running down the hall to alert more third-floor residents.

The women's dorms were faculty-designed campus chastity belts. At ten-thirty p.m.—an hour later on weekend nights—they were locked up tight. The men couldn't enter and the women couldn't leave. It stood to reason that in a moment of passionate, springtime insanity the women's dorms would be targets.

The street had become quiet again, so with a deep breath and great resolve I sat down and opened my metallurgy blue book.

For hours I grappled with the exam, trying hard to ignore the juicy reports of the mob's escapades filtering back to Allen Rumsey. They had thundered into the lounges at Betsy Barbour and Helen Newberry over on State Street—then into the Stockwall and Mosher-Jordan lounges on Observatory Hill. Things got more interesting at Alice Lloyd Hall. The women were prepared. They locked the front doors and doused the interlopers with wastebaskets full of water thrown from upper-story windows. Some women didn't bother to empty the wastebaskets and merely chucked the whole thing on the mob.

But one less-than-hostile Alice Lloyd resident coyly displayed a flashing red light in her window. This drove the mob into a frenzy. They located an unlocked side door and stormed in—invading the rooms—snatching bras and panties from dresser drawers. Thus inspired with a new-found purpose, the mob mounted a second onslaught on the Observatory Hill dorms. A label was immediately affixed to the assaults—*Panty Raids*.

The evening wore on and self-appointed Allen Rumsey couriers breathlessly brought in the latest bulletins from the panty-raid front. Deborah Barker, the Dean of Women, had joined the defense forces, making impromptu personal appearances in an attempt to fend off the more-aggressive invasions. The Women's League building was attacked. The mob marched into the State Theater, ran onto the stage, and gave the startled audience a few choruses of the Michigan fight song—"The Victors."

Around midnight, my roommate burst into the room.

"They ran through the *front* door of the Michigan Union," Rosenkranz cried.

"The panty-raiders? Why would they want to attack the Union?" I asked.

"No... no... it's a mob of *women!*"

"Women? There's a mob of *women* out there? Th'*front* door of the Union? That's illegal."

"It's a *mob*, stupid—a retaliatory raid," Rosenkranz said. "They're getting even for the panty raids on the women's dorms."

"Where are they now?" I asked.

The answer was immediate. Voices carried in through the open window. A horde of women were marching down Madison Street, coming from the direction of the Michigan Union. Rosenkranz and I had ringside seats at the window.

The women immediately attacked the South Quad. Some South-Quad guys hastily formed a barrier at the front door but there were too many women. The South Quadders were trampled under a screaming mass of coeds invading the building.

But half the mob had veered off and were heading toward the Madison Street entrance of Allen Rumsey, right below our window.

"Ohmigawd," I whispered. "They're comin' *here*. Whaddathey want?"

"They want our underwear," Rosenkranz replied soberly.

"You kiddin'?"

"Figure it out. The men grabbed theirs. Now they want ours."

The noise from the street got louder as the women rolled over a group of hapless Allen Rumsey defenders at the Madison Street entrance.

"We can't let 'em in *our* room," I whispered to Rosenkranz.

Rosenkranz, intrigued with the possibility of women invading our room, laughed. "Why not? Just flip 'em a coupl'a pair of your skivvies t'satisfy 'em. Mebbe we can even get names and phone numbers."

I reached in a dresser drawer, grabbed a handful of shorts, and thrust them in Rosenkranz's face. "Don'cha remember this—last fall when I screwed up an' washed 'em with my socks?"

My shorts came in a wide inventory of colors. Some were forest green. Others were spotted like blue Guernsey cows. *None* of them were white.

"Those'll certainly be better trophies than my white ones," Rosenkranz observed.

"My mother inked my name in every pair, and I'm the *only* Harju at Michigan," I cried.

"You'll be famous," Rosenkranz said.

I quickly began stuffing underwear under my mattress.

"They want our underwear."

Friday, March 21st, 1952
West Engineering Building

As I predicted, it had been an all-nighter. Several wrathful females, bent on revenge, had invaded Allen Rumsey but fortunately confined their pillaging to the first floor. My underwear stayed safe. However, by the time things settled down enough for me to finish off the metallurgy exam, the sun was up.

Bleary-eyed, I staggered into the eight-o'clock metallurgy class in West Engineering. Judging from the haggard faces, most of the class had either been panty-raiders or had pulled all-nighters too.

Professor Stielhaus strode vigorously into the room, put his briefcase down, and snapped his fingers. "Okay, gentlemen, let's have your blue books."

One of the students, Gregory Duncan—always able to answer any question brought up in class—put up his hand. "Dr. Stielhaus, as you no doubt realize, an event occurred on campus last night—a rite of spring, if you will. Some of us impulsively participated in this activity which lasted well into the early morning hours, and we weren't able to complete all the problems in the exam."

With a smile, he gazed around the classroom and got several nods of concurrence. "Considering this unforeseen circumstance, we wondered if you might sympathize and extend the blue book deadline until Tuesday morning." Again, heads nodded.

The brazenness of the request startled me. Duncan was sitting there, an audacious you-know-how-it-is-when-women-are-involved smile playing across his face. He was obviously capitalizing on the fact that Stielhaus knew him as one of the brightest students in class who, under ordinary circumstances, would have had no trouble creaming the exam.

Stielhaus stared at him for a moment, bushy eyebrows puckering as he digested what he had just heard. "Mr. Duncan, you're referring to this... this... *panty raid* last night, is that right?"

Duncan nodded.

Stielhaus continued. "So, you feel that this spring frolic should possibly warrant some temporary immunity from my metallurgy exam?"

Duncan nodded again, this time uncertainty flickering in his eyes.

Stielhaus struck a thoughtful pose, gazing at the ceiling with his hands jammed in his back pants pockets. "Gentlemen, we have here a young man who has been forthright enough to bare his escapades and shortcomings to the whole class. I commend him for his candor."

I straightened up with indignation. *What the hell is this?* After keeping my nose clean and wracking my brain all night long to get this damned blue book done, some brown-noser—admittedly a genius—who spent the night going through women's underwear drawers was getting a reprieve and a commendation just because he confessed to it in front of the whole class? I didn't understand Stielhaus's reaction. He wasn't his usual harsh, bastardly self this morning.

Stielhaus fixed Duncan with a hard stare. "I truly appreciate your openness, Mr. Duncan, but indulge me for a moment while I glimpse into the future. Do you think, Mr. Duncan, that the management at Ford Motor Company will delay the redesign of their '58 models if you go in and explain to them that you couldn't complete a blueprint on schedule because you were out stealing women's brassieres?"

Duncan stopped smiling.

Stielhaus leaned down, his face now about a foot from Duncan's. "Or how about North American Aviation, Mr. Duncan?" he rasped sarcastically. "Do you suppose, perhaps, that they might accept a compromised rate of climb on their latest jet fighter when you tell them that your analysis was late because you were otherwise occupied the night before, procuring panties in a women's dormitory?"

Duncan looked away.

"You see, Mr. Duncan, becoming an engineer at Michigan isn't just about achieving *technical* background. We must instill in you the sense of *responsibility* associated with being an engineer."

He turned to the whole class. "Anyone who doesn't have a blue book to turn in this morning will receive a failing grade on this exam."

I handed Stielhaus my blue book as he passed down the aisle. That's more like it, I thought. For a minute there, I was afraid Michigan was turning into some kind of wimpy outfit.

Wednesday, March 26th, 1952
West Engineering Building

My appointment with Dean Emmert was scheduled for two o'clock. I hustled over to his office in West Engineering, eager to hear the details of the White Sands program. I expected he would sit me down and have a one-on-one chat about the co-op program. There were five other engineering students—all looking very brainy—in the outer office, waiting to go into the same meeting.

At two-fifteen, Emmert opened his door and ushered us into a drab, cluttered office. The only chair was the one behind his desk, so the six of us stood while he spoke.

"Gentlemen... a brief description of how this cooperative program will work. If you are selected, you will be a paid, government civil service employee working for the United States Army at White Sands Proving Ground, New Mexico. White Sands is the testing facility for the army's rocket program. The government feels that rockets will figure prominently in the future defense of this country and will also be useful for high-altitude space research. You will work there during the fall and winter months—living right on the Proving Grounds alongside army personnel—then attend school here in Ann Arbor during the spring and summer. This will delay your graduation date somewhat, but the on-the-job training will be invaluable to your career. The program is scheduled to began in mid-September of this year."

Testing rockets—space research—a government civil-service employee —living with the army! And they're going to pay me for this? I fidgeted with enthusiasm, struggling to stand still and keep my mouth shut.

Emmert continued. "The College of Engineering will select twelve students who have completed their freshman year. However, we expect a large number of applicants for the program. Therefore, the selection criteria will be based on scholastic accomplishment."

He stood up, signalling that the briefing was over. "Think it over. If you're still interested, write a letter indicating as much and drop it off with my secretary."

There wasn't anything to think over. As soon as we left Emmert's office, I sat down next to his secretary's desk and wrote my letter.

But I went back to the dorm feeling glum. The letter itself wasn't going to get me into the program. I had to do something about my grades. The panty raid had given me a reprieve in metallurgy, dropping the class average on the take-home blue book sufficiently to give me a B. Now I had to face the problem of passing English and chemistry.

Tuesday, April 8th, 1952
East Hall

In the English 21 classroom I opened up the paper bag, took out the steel game trap, and placed it down on the writing arm of my chair. This greatly aroused the curiosity of the kid sitting next to me.

"What's that?" he asked.

"You'll find out all about it in my speech today," I replied.

Last week I had talked to Orville Banks, the English 21 professor, asking him how I could overcome being scared silly every time I got up in class to give a speech.

"Pick a subject you *really* know," Banks advised. "Something that the audience isn't familiar with... then talk to them about it. Don't *memorize* the speech. Just tell them what you know."

That weekend I prowled the hardware and sporting-goods stores in Ann Arbor and finally found what I was looking for—a steel game trap.

If there was ever a subject I knew something about—that most people didn't—it was trapping. During my teens I had run a trap line during the winter, supplementing my meager allowance by skinning and selling weasel and muskrat hides.

Game traps come in all sizes, the largest being a bear trap, which most people had seen in movie cartoons. But very few had ever seen a real trap, and *nobody*, except grizzled old trappers like myself, knew how to *set* one. Today I was going to give a live demonstration.

When my turn came I walked up to the front of the room, enticingly dangling the trap by its anchor chain.

"Good morning," I stated authoritatively. "I'm here to tell you about the art of trapping for fun and profit." That sentence was the only thing I had memorized.

I glided easily through a brief description of the locales for weasels and muskrats, the type of bait to use, and the skinning and stretching of the furs. The whole class listened. Everyone knew about trappers, but no one had ever heard a speech given by one. Finally, I got to the crux of the matter—the setting of the trap.

A game trap looks like a dangerous device and *is* dangerous. Heavy steel jaws held shut with a large V-shaped spring leave no doubt about its function. I put the trap on my thigh, pressed down on the spring with my left palm, and opened the jaws. "This is the tricky part," I glibly informed the class. "You don' wanna get careless an' lose a coupl'a fingers."

Keeping the spring depressed, I placed the hinged release lever over one of the jaws with my right hand, fastening it to the notch in the trip pan. Deftly yanking my right hand away, I held up the trap—now set—for all the class to see.

But I was saving the best part for last. "Now you adjust the trip pan so it's got hair trigger action." Reaching up from the bottom of the trap—out of harm's way of the business end of the jaws—I carefully tweaked the trip pan, pulling it down ever-so-slightly so the lever holding the jaws open was just hanging on the edge of the trip-pan notch. At the same time I leaned toward the guys in the front row, giving them a really-close view of what I was doing.

"Now when the animal puts just a toe on the trap, it gets him," I said, touching the trip pan from underneath. The trap couldn't grab you if you came at it from the bottom, but of course the average City Joe from Detroit or Grand Rapids didn't know that.

The trap jaws clanged shut with a pistol-like report. Four guys in the front row jumped a foot into the air. Professor Banks, taking notes on my performance, dropped his notebook and pencil.

There were several seconds of stunned silence. Then Banks began applauding, followed by the rest of the class.

Saturday, April 26th, 1952
Allen Rumsey – Room 309

Rosenkranz shuffled the cards, keeping an eye on me to make sure I wasn't peeking at the bottom of the deck. The room was dark except for the light from the gooseneck lamp on Rosenkranz's desk. Cigarette smoke curled lazily in the puddle of light cast onto the green desk blotter.

I didn't have to cheat. I was beating him fair and square. Both of us had bought in for two dollars a couple of hours ago, but now my pile of coins was considerably larger than his.

Rosenkranz put the deck down on the blotter and I cut. We both anted up a penny. He pulled the top card, cupping it in his hand while looking at it. "Seven cents," he said, tossing a nickel and two pennies into the middle of the blotter. I called the bet.

"$4Fe + 3O_2$," Rosenkranz said.

"$2Fe2O_3$," I replied.

Rosenkranz grimaced and tossed the card down. I gathered up the money in the center of the desk.

We were playing chemical poker—a game of our own invention. The deck—painstakingly homemade—contained cards with chemical-reaction equations on them. The dealer drew a card, looked at the equation, and made a bet—the size depending on the difficulty of the equation. His opponent would either call or raise, depending on how smart he felt. The dealer would announce the left-hand side of the equation, and the opponent would have to answer with the right-hand side. If he got it right, he won the pot.

I'd originally made the deck of cards to memorize reaction equations—a last-ditch effort to keep from flunking chemistry. Rosenkranz also had trouble with chemistry and being an inveterate gambler, saw no reason why we couldn't make a game out of it.

Rosenkranz pulled another card. He gave me a Cheshire-cat grin and threw in five nickels. "This one'll cost you twenty-five cents."

I knew he had a hairy equation, but I was on a roll that night. I raised him a dime. He called.

"Hah! Try this one on for size." Rosenkranz exclaimed. "$2C_4H_{10} + 13O_2$."

"$8CO_2 + 10H_2O$," I replied.

Rosenkranz threw the card on the desk in disgust. "What th'hell is this? All year long you been bitchin' about not understanding chemistry. You conning me, or what?"

I scooped up the money. "I *still* don't *understand* chemistry," I said. "I jus' memorized all th'equations. Works, too... I'm gettin' better scores on the blue books."

Friday, June 13th, 1952
Allen Rumsey Hallway

I'd never made a long-distance telephone call before. I nervously waited while the operator made the connection.

"That will be forty-five cents for the first thu-ree minutes, sir," she said.

Forty-five cents—jeesuss. I began feeding nickels into the telephone, counting aloud till I got to nine. I hoped the operator had heard nine nickels go in. I should have asked her if it was three minutes starting after you gave it the last nickel or when you first started to talk.

My parents had finally gotten a telephone, although the old man still thought that it was a luxury that would never replace the U.S. mail.

"Hello?"

"Hello, Ma," I yelled into the phone. "It's me."

"Jerry, is that you?" she yelled back.

"Yeah, Ma. How are ya?"

"Where are you?"

"I'm at the dorm in Ann Arbor."

"What's the matter? Are you all right?"

"Sure, Ma. Everything's fine here."

"Then why are you calling? You didn't fail school, did you?" My mother thought a telephone was strictly an emergency instrument.

"No. I had my last final exam yesterday. I think I passed everything. I'm takin' the Greyhound bus tomorrow morning... be home for the whole summer."

"Then, why are you calling?" she yelled again.

"I wanted t'tell ya that I got accepted in a co-op program. Workin' with rockets at White Sands, New Mexico. It starts in September."

"What???" she shouted. "What about college?"

"I'll be goin' to school in the spring an' summer—next summer—an' workin' in the fall an' winters."

"How much is this call costing you?"

"Forty-five cents."

"You could have waited till you got here and told us then."

"I dunno, I guess I got excited an' wanted t'tell ya right away. I jus' found out an hour ago."

"Did you say New Mexico?"

"Yeah. Down by the Mexican border."

"That's way out west. I don't want you going so far away."

"But Ma, I'm gonna have a government civil-service job. I can save up enough during the winter to pay for my school for the rest of the year. You won't have to send me money any more."

"You won't need any more money from us?"

"That's right."

There were several seconds of silence. "Make sure you dress warm down there," she said.

"Your thu-ree minutes are up." the operator said. "Pu-lease deposit forty-five cents for another thu-ree minutes."

I hung up quickly. I suppose I should have said goodbye.

Rockets—A Love Affair

White Sands Proving Ground
September 1952 - January 1953

Monday, September 8th, 1952
Las Cruces, New Mexico

The train began to slow down as it passed small adobe houses on the outskirts of town.

"LAS CRUCES... LAAASSS CRUUUCCCESSS." The conductor walked through the coach, singing his song to make sure all of the passengers were awake. This was the last stop and everyone had to get off.

After two and a half days of staring at the Midwest landscape speeding by the coach window, eating stale baloney sandwiches, and trying to catch a few winks of sleep on a lumpy seat, I hoped to never see another train. The overnighter from Albuquerque was the worst, with long, unexplained stops down the length of New Mexico. But in spite of being hungry, dirty, and tired, I was excited and anxious to get to the White Sands Proving Ground.

Once outside the railroad depot, I started lugging my two suitcases toward the north edge of town and the bus stop for the White Sands shuttle. Even at seven-thirty in the morning, a hot, dry wind hinted that it was going to be a scorcher today. Maybe southern New Mexico stayed hot all year round—I didn't know.

Las Cruces wasn't the Old West town I had expected. The plain, low brick buildings on Main Street looked exactly like the ones in Michigan except these had air coolers above the doors. Also, menus stuck to the front windows of the cafes were printed in both English and Spanish. They advertised food I had never heard of—enchiladas, tacos, and tamales.

The countryside was *definitely* different. There were no trees. It was empty. You could see for miles in any direction. At the edge of town the main street became Highway US70, heading northeast—straight as an arrow—and shrinking to a hairline as it climbed into the mountains on the horizon.

A group of White Sands civilian-employees stood waiting at the shuttle-bus stop, lunch pails in hand and sipping coffee from paper cups.

They were huddled together like a big family, swapping scuttlebutt about the base.

In a separate group, all five of the Michigan students who had been with me at the March meeting in Dean Emmert's office were standing with their luggage. Happily relieved to see some familiar faces, I rushed up and introduced myself to Dale Ray, Niles Meeker, Jim Fordham, Jack Sherman, and Bob Kruger.

"Six down and one to go," Dale Ray remarked.

"What?"

"I called Emmert's office in August," he explained. "There's seven guys in this co-op program. The six of us and one more."

"Seven?" I was surprised. "Y'mean Emmert screened out everybody but *seven?*"

There *wasn't* any screening," Ray declared. "Only seven of us *applied.*"

Two hours later, we were seated in a classroom—a converted wooden army barracks at the proving ground—waiting for our orientation meeting to begin. Somewhere in the building a wall-mounted air cooler noisily struggled to cope with the rising temperature.

A young army officer—his demeanor reeking with leadership—marched into the room. His uniform bristled with razor-sharp creases and shiny, gold second-lieutenant's bars. Judging from the blossoming crop of acne on his face, he couldn't have been much older than the six of us.

After polishing his horn-rimmed glasses with an olive-drab handkerchief, he opened a new leather briefcase, pulled out a manila file folder, and took roll call.

"Does anyone know where Benjamin Spivak is?" he asked, referring to the seventh Michigan student. We shook our heads.

Irritated, he looked at his wristwatch. "It's oh-nine-hundred hours. We must begin without him." He put the file away and launched into the orientation lecture.

"Welcome to the White Sands Proving Ground. I am Lieutenant Lester Tinley of the United States Army. I am your college co-op program facilitator. In this capacity, I am responsible for your training and welfare. If you have any problems in the next four-and-a-half months, contact me directly."

Tinley attempted to clip off the words authoritatively, but a few times his adolescent voice spiraled upward an octave or so.

"First of all, let us discuss rank and pay. As of this moment, you are members of the United States Civil Service, holding the rank of GS-2. The pay is one dollar and twenty-five cents an hour..."

We quickly glanced at one another. *A buck and a quarter an hour? Jeezus!* I'd never made anywhere *close* to that much money.

Tinley continued. "The program has forty-eight students—seven of you from the University of Michigan and the rest from New Mexico A&M in Las Cruces. The A&M students will live in their dorms on campus and commute back and forth, but you Michigan men have the privilege of living right here on the proving ground. You will be housed in the Bachelor Officers' Quarters, or BOQ, and will eat in the Enlisted Men's Mess.

"However, as civilians, you will have to pay for room and board. BOQ rent is twenty dollars a month. A Mexican maid comes in once a week to clean the room and change the bed sheets. The mess meals will cost you five cents for breakfast and ten cents each for lunch and dinner.

"Keep in mind that this is a military base. You won't wear uniforms or be required to stand morning formation, but other than that, think of yourselves as being in the armed forces. And make no mistake, if you get into trouble on base, the M.P.'s will put you in the guardhouse." Tinley paused to make certain that we fully appreciated the gravity of this information.

The door opened, and a guy sauntered in carrying a suitcase. He wore sunglasses, but I recognized him instantly because he *always* wore sunglasses. With his free hand he was clicking together a pair of drumsticks in time to some inaudible rhythm.

"Are you Benjamin Spivak? Tinley asked.

Click, click, clickity-click-click. Click, click, clickity-click-click. "Yeah, man. That's me."

No one in Allen Rumsey knew him as Benjamin Spivak. He was Be-bop. I didn't know Be-bop personally, but he was a familiar figure at our dorm. He was a freshman engineering student and like J. R. Moon, had an obscenely high IQ and didn't find it necessary to spend much time hitting the books. Instead, he incessantly banged away on his set of drums in the Allen Rumsey basement, often disrupting serious and informative television programs in the lounge, like "Kukla, Fran, and Ollie" and "The Ed Sullivan Show."

"You have missed some valuable orientation information, Mr. Spivak." Tinley said stiffly. "You will have to get it from the others since we must stay on schedule."

Nodding vaguely, Be-bop sat down, still clicking his drumsticks.

Tinley continued. "From here we will proceed to the Security Center where you will be fingerprinted, photographed, and given an interim Confidential ID card and badge. In several weeks, you should receive your Secret clearance, at which time you will be issued your permanent ID and badge."

Tinley lowered his voice to a confidential level. "That clearance, of course, is dependent upon a successful background investigation conducted by the FBI. At this moment, agents are in your hometown, seeking information from your friends and neighbors regarding your moral character."

That jolted me. FBI agents in *Republic, Michigan?*—asking about *me?* Could they even *find* Republic, Michigan?

"After you have finished at the Security Center you will be given the rest of the day to get settled into your quarters," Tinley said. "But at oh-eight-hundred hours tomorrow you will report for duty at your assigned organizations."

Tinley snapped his briefcase shut. "Gentlemen," he said, his voice resonating with patriotic fervor, "tomorrow you will began associating with the most brilliant minds in the field of rocket science. The knowledge and training you are about to receive here at White Sands will help to propel the United States into the 1960's as the undisputed world leader in rocketry!"

Hearts thumping with pride, we picked up our suitcases and followed him out the door.

It was almost noon by the time we were fingerprinted, photographed, and badged. The next stop was the BOQ. Luggage in hand, we trooped behind Lt. Tinley along an asphalt road awash with drifting desert sand.

The Bachelor Officers' Quarters—our home for the next four and a half months—was one in a long row of Quonset huts—gigantic tin cans with tiny windows cut into the sides—plunked in the sand at the edge of the base and used to house civilian workers.

Tinley unlocked the door. A wave of hot air—hotter than the outside—hit us as we entered. Tinley flicked the switch on the air cooler mounted above the door. A large fan spun to life with a deafening roar that vibrated the entire hut like a tuning fork. A torrent of damp, frigid air rocketed through the building, instantly converting the hut into an igloo.

"Every building on the base has an air cooler, so you don't have to be concerned about the heat," Tinley remarked casually, wiping the moisture from his glasses as the temperature plunged below the dew point.

The interior of the hut was divided in half by a narrow hallway with small cubicles on each side made from seven-foot-high plywood sheets. We all picked a "room" and began to unpack. Each cubicle was the size of a jail cell. Everything—walls, floor, furniture, bunk blankets—was olive drab. By comparison, the West Quad looked like a luxury hotel.

Tinley interrupted us, pointing to his watch. "The mess hall will be closing in twenty minutes. You had better hurry if you want your noon meal."

Being a second lieutenant, Tinley had no intention of eating at the Enlisted Men's Mess. He dropped us off and went to the Officers' Club to dine with his peers. The rest of us joined a scraggly line of GI's filing into the mess hall.

One of them behind me struck up a conversation. "Must be gettin' close to your payday, huh?"

"No," I said. "We just got here."

"That explains it," he said. "Civilians never eat here unless they're broke or just don't know any better."

Inside the door, a corporal collected a dime from me. I grabbed a battered, compartmented aluminum tray and a set of eating utensils punched from sheet metal and proceeded toward a long steam table.

A line of lethargic GI's on KP duty were dipping large spoons into big pans and casually tossing food in the general direction of the trays. Something landed on my tray with a mushy plop.

"What is that?" I asked the GI who had served it up.

He looked at me with indignant surprise. No one spoke in the chow line.

"Swiss steak," he snapped. "Wazzit look like?"

I kept on moving. Next, a load of undercooked lima beans clattered noisily onto my tray. A well-aimed scoop of gray mashed potatoes scattered the beans. Things looked up when I received a slab of vanilla ice cream, but I lost interest when a misdirected ladleful of gravy intended for the potatoes landed on top of it.

We silently ate our lunch at a long mess table, feeling uneasy about our quasi-military existence. But Niles Meeker, an innocent, baby-faced kid from Nashville, Tennessee, was optimistic.

"So the living quarters and the food aren't the best," he said cheerfully. "It's worth it to work with the cream of the crop in rocket technology."

"I hope you're right," I said, scraping the gravy off my vanilla ice cream.

At seven p.m., following the operator's instructions, I fed a handful of coins into the pay phone at the Enlisted Men's Club. After a long series of clicks and other noises, I heard the first ring. I closed the booth door so as not to disturb the beer drinkers at the bar.

"Hello?"

"Hello, Ma? It's me," I yelled.

"Jerry... is that you? What's wrong? Are you okay?"

"I'm fine, Ma. Remember? You wanted me to let you know that I got here okay."

"I thought you'd write a letter. How much is this costing you?"

"Don't worry about that, Ma. I'm gonna be making good money... a dollar twenty-five an hour," I shouted. "I'm a GS-2 in the Civil Service now."

"Why are they paying you so much? You don't even have a college degree yet."

"I dunno. There must be good money in testing rockets."

"You be careful with those things. Remember how you burned your fingers that one Fourth of July. Have you got a nice place to stay?"

"Well... I got my own room. Kind'a small. A maid comes and cleans it up, though."

"A *maid?* You should be saving all that money and not hiring maids. Didn't I teach you to clean your own room?"

"She comes with the room... I mean, a maid cleans *everybody's* room."

"What's it like there?"

"It's an army base, but it's kind'a like a town. They have a coupl'a stores, a bowling alley, a movie theater where you can see all the latest shows for twenty-five cents... a place to do your laundry."

"Do they have a church?"

"Yes, Ma. They gotta church."

"Only *one* church? Where do the Catholics go?"

"I dunno, Ma. I think everybody goes to the same church."

"Well... you be sure to go every Sunday."

"Yes, Ma."

"Are they feeding you good?"

"Uh..."

"Eat everything they give you. You're still a growing boy."

"Yes, Ma."

"And you be careful with those rockets."

"Yes, Ma." I looked at my wristwatch to see if my three minutes were up yet.

Tuesday, September 9th, 1952
White Sands Proving Ground

*L*t. Tinley came by the Quonset hut at seven-thirty a.m. sharp. It was his responsibility to get us to our assigned areas so we wouldn't blunder into top-secret places where we didn't belong. An M.P. at the gate to the secure technical area gave our new Confidential badges careful scrutiny.

Tinley provided us with a historical sketch as we walked along. "White Sands Proving Ground was established on July 9, 1945, near the end of World War II. America needed a large land range where missiles could be test fired and recovered after flight for further study."

He waved his hand at the large, corrugated-metal factory buildings and Quonset huts—much larger than the hut we were living in. "Initially, this was going to be a short-term project, so these buildings—intended to be temporary—were put up in a hurry.

"Then, in late August of '45, V-2 rockets captured from the Germans were sent down here. Actually, they weren't rockets at all... just parts of rockets. Three hundred railroad freight cars full of rocket components arrived. The missiles had to be assembled before the army could begin test-firing. We've been testing V-2's ever since. For the last several years we've been building and testing *U.S.-made* rockets, so you can see that this has now become a permanent operation."

My assigned work area—the Climatic Testing Laboratory—certainly didn't *look* like a permanent operation. The lab was a small building with walls of shiny sheet metal and a corrugated-metal roof. A huge pile of metal sheeting, pipes, copper tubing, and spools of heavy wire was stacked along one outside wall.

The interior—except for two cluttered metal desks in one corner—was a jungle of machinery, instrumentation, and otherwise unrecognizable stuff, all interconnected by tubes, ducts, and wires. Gauges sprouted out of every-thing. The strong smell of machine oil and hot solder hung in the air.

Over against one wall a group of men were clustered around a five-foot-high chamber, staring through its glass door at a guy sitting on the chamber floor.

One of the group—a middle-aged man with an iron-gray crewcut and clipped mustache to match—was the only one wearing a white shirt and tie. He appeared to be in charge. He shouted at the guy in the chamber:

"HOW D'YA FEEL?"

"He can't hear ya, Boss," another one said. "That door's got six layers of air-insulated glass."

The fellow inside—a stricken look on his face and in obvious dis-tress—was laboring for breath.

It was a high-altitude chamber. The needle on the gauge registered ten thousand feet but, actually, was barely off the zero point since the calibra-tion markings went all the way up to three hundred thousand feet.

"He still looks okay t'me," said the leader with confidence. "Let's push her up to twelve thousand." He adjusted a dial. A pump at the rear of the lab sprang to life, sucking more air out of the chamber.

Several minutes went by. The fellow sitting inside suddenly panicked and began pushing on the chamber door, trying to get it open.

Someone snorted in disgust. "Don't he know about pressure differential? At twelve thousand feet, we couldn't open that door if we wanted to. Whadda they teach those college guys anyhow?"

The head man got a piece of paper from one of the desks and in large block letters, scribbled out the message, "WE'RE TAKING YOU DOWN," and held it up against the glass. It calmed the guy somewhat. He sat glumly in the chamber while the pump forced air back into the chamber. When the heavy glass door finally opened, he scrambled out with a wild look in his eyes.

"Gawdalmighty, I thought I wuz gonna run outta air an' die in there for sure," he babbled.

The head man gave him a reassuring smile. "Twelve thousand feet is nothing," he scoffed. "When I was piloting P-51's in the war, I never even bothered to put on the oxygen mask till fifteen thousand."

When the group began to break up, I approached him. "Are you Mr. Flint?"

He squinted at my badge, reading my name. "Harju? Oh, you're the Michigan student. Yep, I'm Bob Flint." We shook hands.

"Welcome to the Climatic Test Lab. I run this junkyard," he said enthusiastically. "Whattaya think of our new altitude chamber?"

I nodded my head appreciatively.

Flint clapped his hand on the shoulder of the guy who had just gotten out of the chamber. "Ronny's another co-op student, from New Mexico A&M. He showed up for work this morning with a plugged-up head. I knew how to cure it. So, how're your sinuses feeling now, Ronny?"

Ronny was much calmer now. He snorted experimentally and sucked in air. "Y'know? I think they're better."

"Yep. An old fighter-pilot's trick," Flint declared. "A little altitude keeps the head clear."

I made a mental note never to let him know when I wasn't feeling well.

Flint gave me a quick tour of the lab. Showing me exotic heating and refrigeration chambers, he talked continuously as we carefully threaded our way around the equipment. "Environmental tests on anything the military is interested in... white mice, guidance systems, or whole rockets. Bake it, freeze it... or send it up to three-hundred-thousand feet. Then, see if it still works. Will a Nike missile work the same in an Alaskan winter as it does in a Florida summer? Nobody knows, because nothing like this has ever been done. Believe me, you're getting in at the dawn of a new age."

"Yes, sir!" I exclaimed. "What kind of tests will I be working on?"

"Good... you've got enthusiasm. I like that," Flint said, grinning. "But be patient. We still have a few minor matters to take care of first." He stopped next to a tall, skinny guy working at one of the many benches against the wall. "In fact, let me introduce you to the fellow you'll be working with."

I shook hands with Bill Starzyk who was busily stripping insulation from a rat's nest of multi-colored wires poking out of a pipe extending from the ceiling.

"Ever do any electrical work?" Starzyk asked. "Ever wire up a house?"

"Uh... no." I looked around for some moral support from Flint, but he had already disappeared. "What kind of engineer are you?" I asked Starzyk.

"Engineer? Hell, I'm an electrician. Ain't no engineers in this lab."

"No engineers? How about Mr. Flint?"

"Smart guy... good boss... knows his way around test equipment, but he ain't an engineer. We're all just wrench-and-soldering-iron jockeys around here."

"But he must be pretty good if he supervises all these tests."

"Ain't *been* any tests yet. This whole lab's only been here a month. All those hot'n cold chambers he showed you? None of them are runnin' yet. An' they ain't *gonna* be runnin' until you and I get this building wired."

"I saw the altitude chamber workin'."

That one is," Starzyk admitted. "Some space biology fly-boys over at Holloman Air Development Center, just down the road, want to run some high-altitude tests on white mice next week." Starzyk, smirking, leaned over to me and lowered his voice. "If ya ask me, I think the *real* reason Flint put Ronny in that chamber this morning was to test it out with a human before he put the white mice in there." He chuckled at his own humor. "But seriously, you'll find out pretty quick that we're all just learning on the job. All this stuff with space and rockets is too new. If you college guys figure it out, let me know, would'ja? Meanwhile, let's put ya t'work. Ya ain't afraid of a few electric shocks, are ya?"

Saturday, September 13th, 1952
El Paso, Texas

At six p.m. the army shuttle bus from White Sands pulled up to the El Paso YMCA. Be-bop, Niles, and I, along with forty GI's, piled off the bus. Tonight we were going to celebrate our survival of the first week as engineering trainees in the U.S. rocket program.

Somehow we had also survived a week of eating army food. A week of surly, sweaty GI cooks silently daring us to inquire into the identity of what they were slopping onto our trays. Breakfasts of surplus powdered eggs that had participated in the Normandy landing. Cremated Spam. Desserts swimming in gravy. But tonight would be a blissful reprieve from mess-hall fare. Thanks to Be-bop, we would be dining in style—in Mexico.

Be-bop had arrived from Michigan a week early for the sole purpose of checking out the night life in the surrounding area. Fifty miles south of the White Sands Proving Ground was El Paso, Texas, on the Rio Grande River. According to Be-bop, El Paso was nothing to write home about, but right across the Rio Grande was Juarez, Mexico, a different story entirely. The economy of Juarez, it seems, depended almost entirely on the servicemen from Fort Bliss in Texas, Holloman Air Force Base in New Mexico, and of course, White Sands Proving Ground.

All I knew about Mexico came from watching countless western movies over the years: gay caballeros with silver-trimmed saddles and Gene Autry strumming a guitar while serenading senoritas with flashing eyes. But Be-bop painted an altogether different picture.

"There must be a jillion bars in Juarez," he exclaimed, trying to talk Niles and me into going with him on the weekend. "And they don't care how old you are. You can be nine, nineteen, or ninety-nine, as long as you can pay for a drink. And there are women down there who will do anything—I mean *anything*."

Be-bop's sales pitch had me pawing the ground. However, Niles, the son of a Bible-thumping Baptist minister, was shaking his head in moral indignation. But knowing how thoroughly Niles detested the mess-hall food, Be-bop delivered the clinching argument. "A steak dinner in Juarez—all the trimmings—costs *one* U.S. dollar."

From the El Paso YMCA we walked south to the Rio Grande bridge. The Rio Grande—the famous river where my heroes of the Old West splashed their horses through its sparkling blue waters—was a big disappointment. The shallow muddy water barely covered the ankles of the ragged Mexican kids who were standing in the middle, looking up, and pleading for pennies from the GI's going across the bridge.

"Don't we need a passport or something?" Niles asked as we flowed with the foot traffic crossing the bridge.

"Money's the only passport you need down here, man," Be-bop replied.

The bridge emptied onto Avenida Juarez, a southbound street ablaze with a dense patchwork of neon signs outside hundreds of narrow storefronts housing souvenir shops, restaurants, and bars.

The sidewalks were teeming with people—GI's from the States and Mexican men in open-necked white shirts trying to entice the servicemen into their places of business.

Ancient Chevys, Fords, and Plymouths, all belching blue exhaust and with horns blaring incessantly, clogged the street. Taxis lined the curbs—not Yellow Cabs but old heaps with "TAXI" hand-painted on the doors. The cab drivers were leaning up against the fenders or sitting on the hoods, attempting to drum up business.

One of them tugged on my sleeve and opened the back door of his cab. "Hey, señor, choo wanna come weeth me? I take yoo to Irma's. Lots'a bootiful gurls... all vurrgeens." I hurried along the sidewalk.

Niles was having second thoughts. "Where are we going to get this steak dinner?" he asked apprehensively, brushing aside a kid who had started to shine Niles's shoes as we walked along.

"It's down on the next block... a nice restaurant," Be-bop assured him.

El Palacio Cristal *was* nice—much quieter than the street, with subdued lighting and white tablecloths. An impeccably attired waiter quickly seated us and provided menus printed in English.

We ordered filet mignons, the Cadillac of beefsteaks. When the waiter took our drink orders, Niles requested water.

"No, man, you don't drink the water down here," Be-bop advised. "You play it safe and drink beer." The waiter nodded his head in agreement. Be-bop explicitly described Montezuma's Revenge, and even though Niles had never drunk anything alcoholic, he relented. The waiter brought three beers.

"Hey señor, choo wanna come weeth me?
I take yoo to Irma's. Lots'a bootiful gurls... all vurrgeens."

The meal was delicious and to facilitate good health during our stay in Mexico we ordered another round of beer. The indignities of mess-hall food were dimming.

"I know a place with a hot floor show," Be-bop announced with a leer.

We both nodded our heads enthusiastically. The two beers were beginning to loosen Niles's strict Baptist upbringing.

Back on the street, we quickly made our way over to La Gallina Desnuda, a nightclub. A trumpet blaring a Mexican love song filtered through the closed door.

The dim interior was filled with sweet-smelling Mexican cigarette smoke. A horseshoe-shaped bar enclosed an elevated runway lit by small spotlights. The floor show hadn't begun yet.

"Beee-bop!" a female voice shrilled out of the gloom. A woman with a dense mane of dark red hair ran up and planted a long wet kiss on Be-bop's mouth. He casually ran his hand up her thigh. They were obviously good friends.

As my eyes adjusted, I saw other women emerging from the darkness. All shapes and sizes, they were dressed alike in tight, glittery dresses.

"Choo wanna buy me a dreenk?" a plump one whispered in my ear, snapping her chewing gum seductively. Heavy perfume mingled with the Juicy Fruit on her breath.

Niles took a sharp breath. His mouth was shaped like an O and his eyes bulged. One of the ladies had a firm grip on his crotch.

"You a cherry, I keen tell," she purred to him.

Be-bop waved them off authoritatively and we took seats at the bar. Over in one corner, a small band warmed up for the next floor show. The drummer smiled and waved at Be-bop, holding up his drumsticks, an invitation to participate. Be-bop shook his head. "I spent some time in here last week," he explained. "These cats don't play my kind of music."

The bartender served us a round of beers. As showtime neared, the place filled up with GI's. Finally, the trumpet player blared out an introduction and a smiling, tuxedo-clad emcee bounded onto the runway.

"Ladieees an' genalmannn... welcome to La Gallina Desnuda! Tonight we breeng you the mos' beeutifool girls in all Mexico... includeeng the star of our program... Desireee! Desireee will reveal everytheeng!"

My pulse quickened. I had never seen a strip show. I hurriedly gulped down the last of my beer, and at the speed of light the bartender slammed a fresh one down in front of me.

With the trumpet leading and the drummer whacking out a thundering downbeat, the band lurched into a rocky version of "Some Enchanted Evening." A young girl in a strapless evening dress slid onto the runway and started bumping her hips in time to the beat. After a few more show tunes she had peeled down to a skimpy bra and G-string, revealing primarily the fact that she should be cutting back on her tamales. She was smiling flirtatiously as if intending to strip further, when the emcee reappeared, clapping his hands. The girl trotted off and that was it.

It was pretty much the same routine with the next two girls. By the time the third girl left the stage, the crowd of GI's was getting surly. The emcee held up his hands for attention.

"Choo have been vurry patient, my friends, but now your patience shall be rewarded. In a moment, Desiree will dance for you. *Desiree weel take eet all off!*" The crowd cheered. Niles stuck two fingers in his mouth, emitting a piercing whistle.

The runway lights dimmed and the guitarist, who had been playing backup all evening, took over and expertly riffed into a flamenco introduction. Somewhere offstage the sharp staccato sounds of castanets and the pounding of heels on the floor made it clear that Desiree's act was going to be different.

With castanets aloft, Desiree stepped boldly onto the runway, head tilted forward, a provocative pout on her blazing-red lips. A tall Spanish comb perched in her jet-black hair. She stared insolently down at the sea of hungry faces around the horseshoe-shaped bar while her wooden heels echoed the dark, languid melody of the guitar.

As the tempo increased, Desiree, castanets clacking, reached down and with a free finger slowly began lifting the hem of her dress, revealing perfect legs clad in smoky hose. A red rose peeked from the top of one stocking.

All conversation ceased. The only sounds were the guitar, the castanets, Desiree's heels, and Niles's rapid breathing. It was getting very warm in El Gallina Desnuda. Without taking my eyes off Desiree, I polished off my second beer.

The tempo of the music increased, and precisely at the crescendo, Desiree reached behind her back and with a single deft motion pulled her dress off, flipping it out of the way. The guitar drifted into a new, more seductive melody. Clad only in a black bra, panties, garter belt, and stockings, Desiree moved slowly up and down the runway, locking eyes with each patron at the bar. Again, the music built to a frenzy, and Desiree, castanets and heels hammering, reached for the back of her bra. Everyone held their breath. Using both hands, she pulled her bra *and her wig* off with one fluid motion.

It was a man.

Stunned silence. Arms outstretched and holding the bra and wig, Desiree stood motionless, smiling and waiting for applause. But the only movement in the room was cigarette smoke curling up toward the ceiling.

The emcee ran onto the runway, laughing and clapping his hands, trying to induce the audience to see the humor of it all and give Desiree a big round of applause. Nothing. Everyone stared in disbelief. Then Be-bop began chuckling. He had seen the act last week.

"I think I'm ready to go back to White Sands," Niles declared solemnly, wiping a fleck of drool from the corner of his mouth.

A large hand reached up and encircled Desiree's ankle before he had a chance to leave the runway.

"Ah dew believe th'man said thet Desireeee wuz gonna take it *all* off an' ah notice thet he's still got his panties on. How about it, Desireeee?"

Desiree struggled to get loose, but the guy—about a two-hundred-and-fifty pounder with a U.S. Army Signal Corps insignia tattoo on a muscular forearm—had a firm hold. There were six empty shot glasses in front of him on the bar.

Guys on both sides of the drunken GI scrambled off their bar stools to get out of harm's way. The flamenco player hurriedly put his guitar in its case. Two large Mexicans normally stationed at the front door headed toward the runway.

"I think you're right, Niles," Be-bop agreed. "It's time to leave." As we hurried out, I could hear glass breaking in La Gallina Desnuda. Somewhere a whistle blew.

At the El Paso YMCA we caught the midnight bus back to White Sands. While everyone else slept on the ride back, a beer headache and my thoughts kept me awake. How could I have gotten so excited watching some guy take his clothes off?

Finally, half listening to the bus tires whine on the asphalt, I settled back into the seat and fell into a restless, dreamy sleep. I was strumming a fiery piece on the guitar, backing up a flamenco dancer. It was okay, though—the dancer wasn't Desiree. It was a Finn girl I used to know in Upper Michigan.

Wednesday, September 17th, 1952
White Sands Proving Ground

ZZZZZAAAAAPPPPP!!!!!

The crescent wrench shot out of my hand and clattered across the floor. A million bumblebees buzzed beneath the skin of my fingers.

"I told'ja to throw the switch on that junction box before ya tried t'connect up that power line," Starzyk yelled over from where he was working.

"I did!" I yelled back, pointing with my good hand at the gray box on the wall.

The wrench had landed several feet away. Gawd! Electricity can do that? This was the second week of my new career as an electrician's helper, and I was praying I'd make it back to Ann Arbor before I got fried to a crisp.

Starzyk came over and unrolled a large pencil-drawn circuit diagram. "Hmmm... sorry. My mistake. That line's hooked up to the other box over at the front door. How's your hand?"

I reached down and tried to pick up the crescent wrench off the concrete floor. My fingers refused to work. "It's numb."

"Four hundred and forty volts'll do that," Starzyk said dryly. He looked at my hand. "No burns. You're okay. C'mon, let's take a coffee break till the feeling comes back in it."

He poured two cups of coffee and we went outside. I waved my hand around in the blazing afternoon sun, hoping that the desert heat might have some recuperative powers.

Next door, the huge, sliding metal doors—normally closed—on the big assembly building were open. Inside, lying horizontally on a metal-truss cradle, was a very large rocket. The business end—a monstrous engine surrounded by four fins—was facing us. The topmost fin reached fifteen feet above the concrete floor.

"What is it?" I asked in a hushed voice.

"A V-2," Starzyk replied.

"The German rocket?"

"We been testin' them here for years. The guys who know anything about rockets say the V-2 is still better than anything we've made so far."

I stepped inside for a better look, not knowing or caring if I was allowed in the hanger. The rocket was almost fifty feet long, painted white with black striped patterns on the fins and fuselage. A section of the nose fairing had been removed, exposing a mass of wiring and strange boxes packed inside. Two GI's and one civilian were standing on a three-foot-high platform, running electrical tests using voltmeters and an oscilloscope.

Starzyk continued. "It's liquid-fueled... modern guidance system... can hit a target two hundred miles away with a ton-and-a-half of high explosives. The Nazis started firing 'em at London in late '44. Coming in at supersonic speed, the Brits couldn't do anything about 'em. Luckily, it was too late in the war to make a difference."

"When they gonna launch the next one?" I asked.

"They're hauling this one out to the blockhouse tonight," Starzyk responded. She's going up early Friday morning. It's the last one they've got."

I swallowed. "The last one? Can we go out and watch?"

Friday, September 19th, 1952
White Sands Launch Area

A t five a.m. Starzyk checked out a pickup truck, and we took off for the V-2 launch. Sandy hillocks lining both sides of the road flitted silently by as we drove through the predawn darkness on the straight six-mile stretch to the launch complex. A coyote darted across the pavement in front of the truck, eyes glowing as he stared at us. Far up the road, a cluster of lights could be seen around the launch area.

Starzyk struck a wooden match on the metal dash of the pickup and lit a cigarette. "I ain't been up this early to see a launch in years, but since it's the last V-2 and your first rocket launch, I figured, what the hell..."

Even though the days were hot, it was cold in the desert at night. The army truck didn't have creature comforts like a heater, and I shivered in a light windbreaker. I was concerned about the darkness. "We gonna be able t'see it when it lifts off, or is it gonna be too dark?"

Starzyk laughed. "Oh, you'll *see* it alright. You'll *really* see it, believe me."

We came to a chain-link perimeter fence surrounding the launch area. A white-belted M.P. stood in front of a gate closing off the road, denying entry.

"This is as far as we can go," Starzyk said, pulling the truck onto the shoulder. "The whole area is buttoned up now, and in a minute those guys are gonna hightail it into the blockhouse for the final countdown."

The V-2 was about two hundred yards on the other side of the fence, embraced by a multi-storied steel gantry and illuminated by a host of portable work lights. People scurried around on various levels of the gantry attending to last-minute details of the launch. A pyramid-roofed, concrete blockhouse—about fifty feet square and thirty feet high—was also situated inside the fence to the south of the rocket.

"How thick're the walls on that blockhouse?" I asked.

"I dunno," Starzyk replied. "Pretty thick. It can take a direct hit from a V-2 comin' back to earth."

"Wha... a direct hit?"

Starzyk exhaled a stream of cigarette smoke and snorted a laugh. "When ya been around here for awhile an' seen a few of these launches, you'll find out that they don't always go as planned. In fact, sometimes these babies blow all t'hell before they even get off the pad. Or if they *do* get off, they might come back down on your head. Right now that V-2's loaded up with almost ten tons of liquid oxygen and alcohol. Have any idea what kind'a fireball that can make?"

A siren wailed from the roof of the blockhouse. The people on the gantry quickly climbed down and began to move the work lights and various other pieces of test equipment toward the blockhouse. The gantry was on rails and rolled slowly away from the missile. In a matter of minutes, there was no one in sight. Even the M.P. at the gate had disappeared. The V-2 was sitting alone on the launch pad, lit only by high-intensity lights. Midway up the rocket a long wisp of oxygen vapor was curling out and drifting into the sky.

A speaker mounted on the blockhouse blared:

"X MINUS TEN AND HOLDING."

"Whazzat mean?" I asked.

"Radar Station C and the camera stations up the range are doin' final equipment checks. When they all report into the blockhouse, they'll start the countdown at ten minutes."

After several minutes, the speaker reported:

"X MINUS TEN AND COUNTING."

Other people had driven up from the base to watch the launch along the road near the gate. I'd told the Michigan guys about the launch but couldn't tell if any of them were there.

"X MINUS FIVE."

I was getting excited. "Too bad we can't get any closer."

Suddenly, Starzyk started up the truck. "I know a place." He drove across the road and began bouncing down a two-rut road along the outside of the chain-link fence, following it north. The fence angled in toward the V-2 launch pad.

Starzyk stopped the truck and we got out. Now we were visibly closer to the V-2. Empty Coke and beer cans scattered about in the sand indicated that this spot was known to other rocket watchers. I waded through the deep sand and made my way over to the fence.

"There's no wind... that's good," Starzyk remarked. "Too much wind and they'll delay the launch."

The V-2 was now to the east of us, its nose cone sharply silhouetted against the pearl-gray predawn horizon. The dark sky above our heads was littered with millions of stars. I'd never seen that many stars in a Michigan sky.

"X MINUS TWO."

The metallic voice from the speaker—louder at our new position—startled me.

"Get on this side of the truck," Starzyk advised, walking around to put the pickup between himself and the fence.

I had my fingers laced into the chain-link fence. "Why?"

"In case somethin' goes wrong, the truck'll be a shield."

"X MINUS SIXTY SECONDS."

I fished an Old Gold out of my shirt pocket and, with trembling hands, lit it. I never smoked before breakfast, but this morning I had to do something with my hands. Reluctantly, I tramped back through the sand and joined Starzyk behind the truck.

"X MINUS THIRTY SECONDS."

"I wish we could'a got closer."

"This is close *enough*," Starzyk muttered. "Mebbe *too* close."

"NINETEEN, EIGHTEEN, SEVENTEEN, SIXTEEN..."

The sun hadn't come up yet, so it must have been chilly as hell, but I was getting warm and unzipped my windbreaker. Starzyk started to crouch, his eyes just peering over the wall of the truck-bed. I just stood there.

"FIVE, FOUR, THREE, TWO, ONE..."

The V-2 engine lit up like a gigantic flashbulb, bathing the whole area with instant daylight. The sand became stark white. The white-hot light was quickly diffused by the horrendous cloud of dust kicked up by the rocket engine. Then, the noise and the shock wave hit me.

My gawd, we're too *close!* We're too *close!*

Afterward, I was never quite sure if I had been yelling this at Starzyk or if it had just been my mind screaming. Starzyk couldn't have heard me anyway.

The ground shook. I turned away and crouched down, trying to steady myself by digging my fingers into the steel rim of the truck bed. But the truck was buffeting badly and wasn't much support.

Squinting my eyes I risked a look at the rocket, still unable to look directly at the brilliant plume. The V-2 was off the ground but for a second seemed to hang there, hammering the pickup truck and the two of us with huge rapid-fire shock waves—meting out punishment for sneaking in too close. It had created its own sandstorm, scouring the skin off my face and making a nasty hissing sound against the side of the truck. My open windbreaker was flapping wildly. I had no idea what happened to my cigarette.

Now, the V-2 was gaining altitude and travelling swiftly. I kept watching. Suddenly I was gasping for air—I had forgotten to breathe.

Starzyk honked the horn. He had started the engine and I hadn't even noticed. My neck muscles were complaining violently from looking straight up for so long a time. The air was still again.

"Let's go... show's over," Starzyk said, like nothing had happened. "I wanna get some coffee before work."

I looked over at him, but the rocket plume was still a bright image on my retina, totally obscuring his face. Without answering, I turned back to the V-2 in flight. It was way up there now, the rising sun reflecting off its vapor trail condensing in the atmosphere.

Suddenly something strange happened. Not being familiar with the way rockets worked, I didn't know if it was normal or not, but it appeared as though the V-2 was in two pieces. The vapor trail wobbled, breaking the smooth trajectory it had been carving across the sky.

"Hey, Bill," I shouted. "I think you better take a look."

Starzyk instantly jumped out of the truck and produced a pair of binoculars, training them on the V-2. "Uh-oh... problems."

"What... what?"

He continued tracking the missile with the binoculars. "Not sure, but it looks like the engine broke loose." He handed me the glasses.

Using the binoculars, I had to search the sky for several seconds before I found the V-2. The missile looked intact, but it was rolling and fishtailing aimlessly around the sky—definitely out of control.

The V-2 was off the ground but for a second seemed to hang there, hammering the pickup truck and the two of us with huge rapid-fire shock waves.

I realized that I was looking straight up at it. "Jezzus, Bill. It's right over our heads."

Starzyk took the binoculars and tracked the stricken rocket. "Hard to say... it must be three, four miles up and at that altitude you can't tell exactly *where* it is."

I looked over at the main road near the gate. Many of the spectators who had been standing there watching the launch were starting up their vehicles to flee to safety.

"I think we better get the hell outta here," I said quietly.

Starzyk shook his head. "Where ya gonna go? Look how high it is. It could glide over to the base and clobber you while you're sitting in the front pew of the church. Where we're standing right now might be the safest place on the range. Might as well relax and watch the show."

"Think we ought'a get under the truck, though?"

Starzyk laughed. "If that rocket decides to hit this truck, it'll pound it twenty-five feet into the sand."

For what seemed like an hour, but was probably only about a minute, the V-2 tumbled erratically high above our heads. Finally, as it lost altitude, it got bigger and bigger. During the final seconds of its descent, the rocket stabilized and plunged into the earth like a giant dart, well to the south of us. A large, black mushroom-shaped cloud appeared on the horizon, followed by a muffled explosion.

It was finally over, but on the drive back to the base I could hardly sit still. Images of the whole experience were vivid and alive in my mind. No drug in the world could have produced the fantastic high I was on. From that moment on, I knew I was going to be a rocket engineer.

Friday, November 28th, 1952
White Sands Launch Area

It never failed. Around six-thirty in the morning, toward the end of the graveyard shift—no matter how much coffee I'd drunk—I'd get sleepy as hell. Sipping my eighth cup of the night, I took out my old man's letter and reread it.

Hello Jerry,

Everything is OK here. Lots of appleknockers drove up from Detroit for deer season but there's too much snow and not too many are getting their buck. They still drive way out of town and don't look for sign close in. If they did they'd see the tracks of that old buck in the cemetery. He's still waiting for you, though he's going to stay in the swamp now if the snow gets much deeper.

Good to hear you're learning something useful. Electricians make good money. Ma was glad that you're coming back to school in February. For awhile we thought you might quit and stay out there in the desert.

Pop

The desert wind hammered the twenty-foot army van with violent, random gusts, seemingly getting worse as the sun rose. Ronny Garcia, Bob Flint's other co-op student, and I were working night shift, crammed inside the van with a large array of temperature recorders. We were out at the army blockhouse area monitoring cold-temperature conditioning of a Nike Ajax antiaircraft missile.

The Nike was mounted on its launcher but in a horizontal stand-down position. The whole system was snugly enclosed in a forty-foot-long, thickly insulated, canvas-covered blanket supported by a lightweight metal rib cage. The blanket was made in several sections, all joined together by heavyweight zippers for quick dismantling. It was connected by two fifteen-inch-diameter flexible ducts to the Field Refrigeration Unit or FRU—a Rube Goldberg device designed by Bob Flint. The FRU was a custom-made, insulated aluminum box on a small trailer. It had a built-in 220-volt fan—getting power from the blockhouse—that blew air through a deep-freeze-size chamber containing dry ice. The cold air shot through the entry duct into the blanket, across the missile, out the exit duct, and back into the FRU. The fan was louvered to increase or decrease the flow, thereby regulating the air temperature. Surprisingly, the damned thing worked really well as long as you kept it filled with dry ice.

Dry ice—solid carbon dioxide, super-cold at more than one hundred degrees below zero—had to be handled carefully with heavy gloves. If you grabbed a chunk with a bare hand, you were instantly frozen to it. We had a plentiful supply at the launch site under a canvas tarp. Whoever was monitoring the test had to break up blocks of dry ice with a sledge hammer from time to time and shovel them into the FRU.

The Nike and its booster had thermocouples taped all over their surfaces to monitor temperatures. It had taken almost five days—twenty-four-hours a day—of constant cooling to drive the temperature of the long missile and its booster down to forty below zero. But that's where we had it now. In an hour we were going to jerk the insulated blanket off the rocket and army personnel would quickly raise the missile to launch position and fire it at an aircraft drone to see if the Nike would function at cold temperatures.

I had "graduated" from being an apprentice-electrician. Starzyk and I had finally gotten the Climatic Test Lab wired up by mid-October, and the fact that no one was electrocuted apparently qualified me to move on to bigger and better things.

Frankly, I wasn't convinced that my present job was a bigger and better thing. For five straight days I'd been working from midnight to eight in the morning, dutifully entering recorder temperatures into a log book and shovelling a hundred tons of dry ice into Flint's infernal machine. I spent hour after hour watching the long, slender, metal ink pens on the recorders slowly scrawl out missile temperatures on circular graph paper which rotated once every twenty-four hours. I was sinking into a stupefied trance with my stomach gnawing from massive doses of black coffee. We had a portable radio in the van, but tonight the only thing that was penetrating the sandstorm was some million-watt station in Del Rio, Texas, featuring country ballads about lost love, cheap whiskey, fast cars, and faster women. The "music" was liberally interspersed with commercials hawking lifelike plastic religious icons.

It was Ronny's turn to watch the recorders. He stuffed the remains of a Mounds bar into his mouth as he scooted up and down the van's narrow aisle on a castered stool. "Temperature on the booster fin's gettin' up to minus thirty-eight, an' the louver's been wide open for an hour now."

"More dry ice," I muttered, putting down the old man's letter.

Ronny produced the deck of playing cards that we used to determine who would smash and shovel the dry ice. I drew the four of clubs. Ronny smiled as he drew the jack of spades. He chortled triumphantly. How does he *do* that? I'd lost three straight draws and had been smashing and shovelling dry ice all night long.

I struggled into my jacket, grabbed my gloves, and went outside thinking that at least the dry-ice smashing and shovelling was keeping me awake.

I'd no sooner negotiated the narrow metal steps from the trailer door to the concrete launch-pad when I got smacked in the head by a flying tumbleweed. I'd never get used to the winter sandstorms on the desert. Tumbleweeds the size of small automobiles hurtled through the air—some more than a hundred feet up—while the howling sand was scouring paint off of cars and buildings. Michigan winters were bloody cold, with deep snow, but at least snowflakes didn't leave scars.

I smashed up three blocks of dry ice and shovelled the pieces into the refrigeration unit. By now it was daylight and vehicles were arriving from the base to support the Nike launch. Flint and Starzyk drove up in a large army truck just as I was adjusting the fan louver. The three of us went into the van. Flint glanced at the recorders and nodded approvingly at the Nike's stabilized temperature readings.

"Well, this is the day we'll see if that frozen popsicle out there gets off the pad," exclaimed Flint in a loud, vigorous voice, trying to pump some enthusiasm into Ronny and me.

"I'm glad to hear that," I replied wearily. "After five nights of staring at those recorders and shovelling dry ice, I'm ready for something to happen."

An army captain stuck his head in the van door. "We're gonna start the live countdown now, at X minus thirty minutes. We want to keep the missile cold until the last possible moment, so at X minus five minutes you need to shut down the refrigeration unit, yank that cover off, and get everything clear of the launcher as quickly as possible. Will that be a problem?"

"Nope. Can do," Flint replied confidently.

Five minutes? I had helped put that blanket on the Nike last week, and it took a helluva lot longer than five minutes.

As if reading my thoughts, Flint said, "It'll come off a lot quicker than what it took to put it on."

With only a half hour left on the test, it wasn't necessary to continue monitoring the missile temperatures, so we snipped all the thermocouple wires. Starzyk hooked up the instrument van to the pickup truck and pulled it away. All that was left near the rocket on its launcher was the FRU on the small trailer, the Nike blanket, and the connecting ducts.

Starzyk returned with the truck and hooked the FRU trailer up in readiness. We kept the FRU running but removed all the nuts and bolts on the input and exit ducts, so we could quickly pull them loose from the blanket. The plan was to yank the flexible ducts off the blanket, pull the FRU trailer away with the truck, unzip the blanket, dismantle the rib cage, and drag it all away from the launcher by hand.

"X MINUS FIVE MINUTES."

We sprang into action. The exit duct came off easily, but when Starzyk and I grabbed the frosty input duct and gave it a pull, it didn't budge. It was frozen fast to the metal connector flange on the blanket. Starzyk whacked at it with a hammer. No luck.

Flint thought fast. "Remember that heavy metal brace welded across the inside of the mouth of the duct? We need somebody inside the blanket to hit that brace outward with a hammer. That ought'a do it." He glanced around at his crew. "Gotta be somebody who can crawl in there without disturbing the missile. Somebody slim. How about you, Ronny? You're the smallest."

Ronny turned pale. "Me, Boss? It's forty below zero in there. I'll freeze my ass off." Ronny Garcia had been born and raised in warm, sunny Alamagordo, New Mexico, just down Highway 70 from the proving ground.

"X MINUS FOUR MINUTES."

We were running out of time. Flint quickly turned to me. "I think you'll fit... you're from up north and used to the cold. Can you do it?"

"I can try," I gulped.

Starzyk slapped the hammer and a flashlight into my hand. Flint stripped off his jacket, and I put it on over mine. The aft end of the blanket was unzipped just enough for me to get in.

As I was about to enter, Flint said "You'll only be in there for about a minute, so you should be okay, but we're gonna keep the fan running while you're inside, 'cause we gotta keep the missile as cold as possible."

I crawled into the blanket and turned on the flashlight, playing the light beam across the three white, frosty metal booster fins directly in my path. As soon as I got in, Starzyk zipped up the blanket again to keep warm air from leaking onto the missile.

The metal rib cage supporting the blanket allowed just enough space around the Nike and its booster for the cold air to circulate freely, but it wasn't designed for someone to go in there and work. I barely had enough space to move. I carefully picked my way between two of the booster fins and pushed forward to the input refrigeration duct.

In the dim light of the flashlight, the white booster and Nike missile extended forward into the murky gloom. I had the eerie feeling that I was on a distant planet creeping through a crypt containing the corpse of some stubby-winged, alien monster bird—except this monster wasn't dead. It was very much alive, with a half ton of high explosives in its belly.

It was cold—I mean *really* cold. I had forgotten what forty below zero felt like—and I wasn't dressed for it. In a matter of seconds the numbing cold penetrated my clothing and permeated my arms, legs, toes, and fingers. Breathing was terrible—the air felt like ground glass entering my lungs.

Since we were so close to the blockhouse, the loudspeaker penetrated the thick insulated blanket.

"X MINUS THREE MINUTES."

I tried to forget the debilitating cold and scrambled forward alongside the long booster. The input air duct was just aft of the Nike tail fins. If I'd thought it was cold back at the booster fins, it was like Miami Beach compared to the blast of frigid air coming from the input duct.

Holding the flashlight with my left hand, I swung the hammer, hitting the iron cross brace welded across the mouth of the duct in an attempt to break the duct loose from the blanket flange.

Nothing happened. I hit it again. Still nothing. I swung the hammer high over my right shoulder for greater impact. It slipped out of my frozen fingers, clanging against the Nike engine fairing.

I desperately played the flashlight beam around my feet, looking for the hammer. I quickly found it and shined the light on the Nike to see if any damage had been done. Tough missile—it hadn't even chipped the white paint.

"X MINUS TWO MINUTES."

I couldn't believe this—a half hour ago I had been bored out of my skull with the job. Now, panic stricken, I savagely hammered on the cross brace over and over again. It wouldn't look good at all on my performance record if the army had to halt the countdown because I was practically sitting on the missile.

But WOULD they *stop* the countdown? Hell, that captain probably didn't even see me go inside this thing. Flint had assured them that we'd have the blanket off and clear in plenty of time. He wasn't in the blockhouse to tell them what was going on. The Nike had undergone hundreds of test firings—what if they didn't even look out of the blockhouse viewing port before they raised the launcher and fired? Nah... that's crazy!

With ragged, sobbing breath I braced my left hand on the Nike and gave the cross brace a gawdawful smash with the hammer.

Daylight appeared as the duct fell outward. The blanket walls immediately began to come apart at the seams as Flint, Starzyk, and Garcia quickly unzipped it. I jumped out and frantically pitched in. In a matter of seconds we had the thing dismantled and were dragging it away from the launcher. Starzyk jumped in the truck, ground the gears, and sped off with the refrigeration unit trailer in tow.

"X MINUS SIXTY SECONDS."

We had no sooner moved the blanket and its frame away when the launcher's hydraulic motor started raising the Nike and its booster to its near-vertical launch position. The four of us dashed for the blockhouse door. As I entered, I glanced up and saw the contrails of an old World War II fighter—a Grumman Wildcat—being used as a target drone. It was flying in an oval pattern high above us, waiting for the Nike to come and get it.

In the crowded control room inside the blockhouse, I hurriedly jockeyed for position at the thick, multi-paned window to watch the show.

"SIX, FIVE, FOUR, THREE, TWO, ONE..."

By now I had witnessed several launches and they were always impressive. With a bright flash of flame from the booster, the missile shot off, shaking the massive blockhouse with an awesome shock wave. The Nike was so much faster than a V-2 that within a second it was out of sight above the window.

The army guys intently watched an array of tracking scopes, at the same time barking sequencing commands into microphones to the down-range camera stations.

"Contact!" reported a corporal watching an oscilloscope.

Another guy let out a shrill whistle and a few others clapped. The missile had made the required near-miss rendezvous with the Wildcat drone, as the drones were too expensive to destroy.

The test was a success—at forty below zero the Nike Ajax performed as required.

The captain in charge grinned and shook Flint's hand. "Good work. For a minute there I thought you wouldn't get that thing off the missile in time and we'd have to stand down. Guess you had the timing figured out all along, didn't you?"

"That's correct, Captain," Flint said modestly.

I started to shiver. The forty-below-zero exposure had caught up with me. I had no feeling in one of my ears lobes. I rubbed it furiously, trying to get some circulation back into it.

"Still bored?" Flint asked me.

Teeth chattering, I shook my head.

"Working out here's like being a policeman or fireman—long periods of total monotony interrupted by moments of tough decision making and near-death experiences. Gotta get used to it."

Starzyk pressed a paper cup of steaming black coffee into my shaking hands. I promptly spilled the coffee all over my half-frozen thumb, thawing it out instantly.

Friday, January 30th, 1953
Climatic Testing Laboratory

Four p.m.—the final day of my first stint at White Sands. I gathered up my personal belongings from around the lab and stopped to say goodbye to Flint.

"Well, sir, this is it," I said. "We're leaving for Ann Arbor tomorrow."

He shook my hand. "What did you think of your job here?"

"I liked it very much," I said earnestly. "I'm looking forward to coming back." I meant it, too. It had been an exciting four-and-a-half months. Just as he promised on the first day, Flint had involved me in all sorts of tests ranging from high-altitude experiments with white mice to freezing Nike missiles. School was going to be dull by comparison.

"You'll have had some thermodynamics by the time you come back, won't you?" Flint asked suddenly.

"Thermodynamics? Uh... no... I won't take that till my junior year. Why?"

"Well, I've got something lined up for you," he said enthusiastically. "Designing a thermal jacket for the Viking missile. Be a big help if you had some thermodynamics under your belt. Can't you bend your curriculum a bit?"

"Uh... y'know they have my courses all set for the first two years. Besides, I have to take two semesters of physics before they even *let* me take thermodynamics."

Flint casually flipped his hand in the air, unconcerned about bureaucratic obstacles like prerequisite courses. "Hey... just buy a thermo textbook and read up on it on weekends."

I gulped. "Y'know, Mr. Flint, I won't be back here till September. You might need that work done sooner than that."

"Don't worry," he said cheerfully. "The job'll be waiting for you when you get back."

Saturday, January 31th, 1953
White Sands BOQ Area

Using a big safety pin, I carefully fastened the handkerchief containing three hundred and forty-six dollars to the inside band of my underwear. The money was saved from my salary at White Sands and would go a long way toward meeting my school expenses during the spring and summer semesters. I closed my suitcase and carried it out to the car. Standing on the hood, I crammed the suitcase onto the towering pile of gear already in the luggage rack on the roof.

In December, it was decided that in order to get back to Ann Arbor economically we needed a car. Any good-sized sedan would do nicely. There were only six of us left now, since Be-bop, concluding that rocket science wasn't exciting enough for him, had returned to Michigan in October.

After a few weekends of shopping around the El Paso used-car lots we found a beautiful 1940 Super-Six Hudson with a new bronze paint job, nice upholstery, and pretty-good brakes and tires.

The first sign of trouble appeared after we drove it back to White Sands. The engine had burned two quarts of oil in fifty miles. It didn't take a rocket scientist to figure out that it would cost a fortune in motor oil to get back to Ann Arbor. Fortunately, Jim Fordham had once *watched* a mechanic install a set of piston rings, so with that experience under our belts, we took the Hudson to the army motor pool where we talked the sergeant in charge into letting us use a few tools and shop space. Fordham performed the ring job, and the rest of us helped out as best we could by handing him wrenches and cold beer.

The engine actually started up when we got it back together, and after a couple of weekends of extensive field testing—driving the car down to Juarez and back—we discovered that the Hudson was now getting an amazing *two hundred miles* to a quart of oil. The operation was deemed a resounding success, and we felt confident in driving the Hudson back to Ann Arbor.

After attending to a million last-minute details everyone finally got into the car. The trunk and luggage carrier were completely full, yet a few insisted on taking even more personal belongings. These items had to be held on their laps.

With all that weight, the Hudson squatted down on the road like a tired old turtle. The heat generated from six warm bodies immediately fogged up the windows. Obviously, we'd have to travel with the front windows partially open, a daunting prospect during a Midwestern winter. Jim Fordham ground the engine to life, and with an agonizing groan the car slowly labored away from the Quonset hut.

It was not going to be an easy trip, driving day and night on Route 66—everyone taking four-hour shifts at the wheel—stopping only for food, gas, oil, radiator water, and using toilets. Barring mechanical breakdowns, this would put us in Ann Arbor on Monday night—plenty of time to register for the spring semester.

Since it was our last day on base, we had to turn the auto-access car permit over to an M.P. at the front gate. A walkie-talkie in his guard shack loudly squawked a countdown—by now a familiar sound to all of us.

"X minus twenty seconds to launch," the M.P. said dryly.

I looked out the car window toward the launch area six miles away, mentally counting off the seconds. At X minus zero, a pinpoint of light rose swiftly from the ground into the morning sky. We were too far away to see the actual outline of the rocket, but from the acceleration and launch angle, I knew it had to be a Nike Ajax.

Love and Calculus

The University of Michigan
February - August 1953

Monday, February 2nd, 1953
Ann Arbor, Michigan

As Jim Fordham eased the Hudson up to the curb in front of the West Quad, students picking their way along the icy sidewalks were startled by the racket our engine was making. It clattered like a fifty-caliber machine gun.

We'd just arrived from New Mexico and none too soon. Midway across Illinois we heard a rapping noise in the engine. It got progressively worse as we got near Ann Arbor.

When the problem began, Fordham promptly diagnosed it as a worn main bearing. The rest of us nodded sagely, although I didn't have any idea what a main bearing was. We had gotten away with doing our own ring job, but Fordham explained that replacing the bearing was considerably beyond his automotive expertise. To make matters worse, he added that the cost of getting a qualified mechanic to do it would far exceed the value of the car.

As Fordham parked the car, the engine died. He jabbed the floorboard starter button with his foot. Nothing happened—not even a groan. The odor of hot oil drifted up from beneath the Hudson's hood.

"That's it," Fordham declared, getting out of the car. "The crankshaft's seized up. She's had it."

"What are we gonna do with it?" I asked with alarm. Somehow, the car had been registered in my name during the purchase in El Paso.

Fordham shook his head. "Leave her here for now. Maybe I'll think of something."

Reluctantly, we emptied the car of all personal belongings. There was nothing else to do. We couldn't afford to get it fixed. All the money we'd saved at White Sands was earmarked for room and board, books, and tuition for the spring and summer semesters.

The Hudson had served us well on the long trip: day and night bravely chugging along Route 66, up and down the Ozark foothills, across the frozen Midwestern grain fields, all the while giving us a respectable eleven miles to a gallon of gas and consuming only ten quarts of oil on the whole trip. Niles, who empathized with all stricken creatures, great and small, choked back a tear as he stroked its fender.

The Hudson's corpse sat at the curb on Madison Street for the next two weeks, and then one day it just vanished, no doubt a victim of the Ann Arbor police impound squad. We never saw it again. I hoped it had gone to the big Hudson heaven in the sky.

Wednesday, February 4th, 1953
Slater's Bookstore

I was waiting at the door when Slater's Bookstore opened at nine a.m. In order to buy used textbooks—much cheaper than new ones—you had to be there bright and early. Quickly latching onto well-tattered editions for my physics, calculus, and third-semester drafting courses, I headed for the rear of the store. A better slide rule now had a higher priority than brand-new books.

The same guy who had sold me the cheap, aluminum slide rule was still behind the display case.

"May I help you?"

I slapped three ten-dollar bills down on the counter. "I want a Post Versalog."

"An excellent choice," he exclaimed, instantly producing a box with a new Versalog slide rule in it.

I brought out my aluminum slide rule. "Can I get anything for this in trade?" Many of the numbers had been rubbed off from frequent handling.

He eyed the old slide rule distastefully. "A couple of dollars, perhaps."

"That's fine."

Trying to be helpful, he took the new Versalog out of its box. "May I point out some of the more advanced features of this fine instrument to you?"

"You already did—a year and a half ago. Wrap it up."

Registration was next. Clutching the Railroad Ticket registration forms, I made my way through the writhing mass of students in the Waterman Gym and got into one of the lines for engineering classes.

A half-hour later, as luck would have it, I faced the same professor who had scheduled my freshman classes in September 1951. The very one who had gleefully given me *five* eight-o'clock classes, destroying any hope of a decent night's sleep during my first semester. He appeared to be chewing on the same unlit cigar.

Snatching the Railroad Ticket from my hand, he began to pour over his class rosters.

"If you don't mind, sir, I'd appreciate it if you'd give me as many eight-o'clock classes as possible," I said.

He paused, slowly raising his head with a puzzled stare. "You *want* eight-o'clock classes?"

"Yessir! I'm an early riser, and eight-o'clocks free up the rest of the day for other obligations."

Dedicated to prevent any student from receiving a comfortable class schedule, he searched my face for a clue as to what I was really up to. I stared him down with baby-faced innocence. Finally, applying himself to the paperwork, he compiled my class schedule and handed it back to me.

I managed to look disappointed. "Only two eight-o'clocks, sir? I was hoping for five."

He grinned. "You kids have to learn that you don't always get what you want in life," he declared sardonically. "Make do with what's given to you. That's the way the world works." He glanced smugly over my shoulder at the guy behind me. "Next."

I quickly walked away before he changed his mind. On the drive up from New Mexico, I had read one of Krugers's books called *The Science of the Mind.* It had a fascinating chapter on reverse psychology.

Monday, March 16th, 1953
West Engineering Building

"**J**eez... will ya lookit that!" Virgil Sternitzky—known to his friends as Letch—exclaimed in a reverent voice.

I was busily taping the partially completed drawing of an air-cylinder end plate to my drafting table, preparing for the one-o'clock advanced engineering drawing class when Letch spoke up from the table behind me. I looked up immediately since Letch normally limited his in-class conversation to half-grunts through clenched teeth as he laboriously etched 6-H pencil lines onto his class projects.

A woman had just entered the classroom. She was loaded down with rolled drawings, triangles, a T-square, and other drafting paraphernalia. Of the two thousand students in the College of Engineering there were only five or six females. Every so often, between classes, I would see one of them flitting silently down the hallways of the engineering buildings. These women weren't much to look at, having adopted protective coloration by not wearing jewelry or makeup. Like the rest of us, they dressed in wrinkled, baggy clothing covered with India-ink spots.

But this one was *different*. She was exceptionally pretty with blonde—almost platinum—hair. Her nicely filled-out light blue sweater was tastefully adorned by a single strand of luminous pearls.

"That's Anne Cathaway," I whispered. "I heard about her. They say she's pretty smart."

"Th'hell you say," Letch uttered, gnawing feverishly on a corner of his forty-five-degree triangle. "How smart kin she be with a body like that? Lookit those bazooms!"

Cathaway walked to the front of the room and handed some paperwork to our drafting instructor, Professor Stibowitz. Stibowitz, no more accustomed to having a female in class than the rest of us, began self-consciously brushing away the thick deposit of chalk dust that had accumulated on his vest over the years. He signed her transfer form and pointed in my direction.

"Sonovabitch," Letch gasped. "She's transferring into our class. An' she's gonna be sitting right in front of you."

Like penitentiary convicts whose prison had just turned coeducational, everyone watched Anne Cathaway walk to the empty drafting table in front of me. She put her stuff away and quickly taped her air-cylinder-end-plate drawing to the tabletop. Since all the advanced drafting classes worked on the same assignments, transfers were commonplace. She turned to me and smiled politely.

I showed her every tooth in my head with an eager grin. Aside from Mrs. Harper, our plump, fiftyish, steely-eyed housemother at Allen Rumsey, I hadn't been close to a female in a long time. My daily orbit between the West Quad and the engineering buildings provided scant opportunity to meet women.

By the end of the first hour, we had finished the air-cylinder-end-plate drawing. Stibowitz gave us our usual break, and Letch and I went to the men's room for a cigarette.

"You see the way she smiled at you?" Letch said with a leer. "Here's your big chance, pal, sittin' right in front of you. Get yerself a date with the best-lookin' engineer at Michigan."

"She wouldn't have anything t'do with me," I replied halfheartedly.

"You kiddin'? Here's what you do. You're pretty good at drafting—offer to give her a hand. Believe me, she'll go for it. From then on, it'll be a piece of cake."

Cathaway didn't return from the break with the rest of us, since the only ladies room in West Engineering was two floors down on the other end of the building. But Stibowitz wanted to talk to the guys anyway, while she was out of the room.

"We must respect the presence of a woman in the class," he said quickly, glancing furtively at the door. "Therefore, I don't feel it's appropriate to use the terms 'male' and 'female' when talking about the various interconnecting hardware parts that appear on the drawings. When the occasion demands, I will be using other words instead."

It was a good idea. One just couldn't spout smutty terms like "male" and "female" in front of a woman.

After the break, Stibowitz began a lecture on our next project: a detailed drawing of a bench lathe.

"The incurvate part of the tool rest clamp..."

Anne Cathaway's hand immediately shot up. "Excuse me, sir. Incurvate? Is that the same as female?"

Stibowitz's face turned crimson. "Uh... why, yes," he said. "Some people refer to it that way. "

I scribbled down "incurvate" for future reference. I was glad she'd asked the question since I'd never heard the word before.

As the final hour dragged by, I couldn't get Letch's advice out of my mind. When the class was over I decided to make my move.

"Uh... excuse me, Miss Cathaway... I just want to say that if you should need any help... with... uh... drafting I mean... just let me know."

Cathaway turned around to respond, and her gaze fell on my completed drawing of the air cylinder end plate that I was about to turn in to Stibowitz. She tapped the corner of my drawing with a well-manicured, bright red fingernail. "You know, the male safety cap on this end plate is supposed to be made out of steel. On your section display you've shown it as cast iron—probably just a goof. You could never make a cap like that out of cast iron—too much pressure. It would blow all to hell."

How could a word like "hell" tumble out of those pouty, red lips? But I looked down at my drawing. She was right.

"Ohmigawd!" I cried. The drawing was due to be turned in immediately, and my cast-iron safety cap had been immortalized in India ink.

Cathaway produced an Exacto knife and offered it to me. "No problem. Just scrape out some of those lines with this... take you about three minutes. Stibowitz won't even notice."

I took the Exacto knife. "Uh... thanks."

"Glad to help," she said, gathering up her stuff.

Letch caught up with me as I was on the way to my next class. "Did'ja get a date with her?"

I shook my head.

"No?" Letch grinned wolfishly. "Hell... if you're not man enough to ask her out, I'll do it myself. *I'm* man enough."

"Letch... you may be man enough, but are you *engineer* enough?"

Friday, June 26th, 1953
Red's Rite Spot
Ann Arbor

Nothing came easy at Michigan, even in the summer. During summer session, students had to take only two courses instead of the usual four or five. I thought this would be a snap until I discovered that the hours were doubled in summer since the classes ran for only eight weeks.

Food was another problem. I'd eaten all my meals in the dormitory, but the West Quad was closed during the summer. The rooming house on East Jefferson where I was staying had no kitchen privileges and eating in restaurants was economically out of the question. So when I heard that Red's Rite Spot, a small lunch counter on William Street, was looking for a dishwasher—seventy-five cents an hour, all meals included—I took the job.

Dishwashing in a restaurant is terrible work. The customers were dirtying cups and plates faster than I could clean them. To top it off, the hot soapy water was turning my hands into boiled lobsters.

The food wasn't bad if you didn't mind a steady diet of grilled hamburgers, grilled ham, and grilled liver and onions. If it couldn't be grilled, Red's Rite Spot didn't serve it.

The job did have one fringe benefit: Red himself. With low prices and fast service Red had more business than he needed, so he didn't bend over backward being nice to customers. The entertainment was first-rate when he dealt with the ones he didn't like.

At noon the joint was packed as usual. Red stopped cooking for a minute, wiped his hands on his greasy apron, and strolled down to the end of the counter to confront, as he put it, "another gawdamn coffee-dawdler."

A coffee-dawdler was someone who lingered, leisurely sipping a cup of coffee after a meal while still occupying a valuable stool. With customers lined up at the door at mealtimes, waiting for a stool, fast turnover was critical if Red was going to make a buck.

The man reading the newspaper over his coffee was obviously a new customer. Otherwise, he would have known Red's unwritten rule—you got your hot meal two minutes after ordering, but you had to eat it in fifteen minutes and vacate the stool for the next customer.

Red thrust a hairy thumb into the guy's coffee and stirred slowly. "Coffee still warm?" he inquired amiably in his cement-mixer voice.

"What the hell!" the man blurted out, staring at Red's big thumb stirring his coffee. Then he looked up at Red.

Red was a big guy—six-foot-four, two hundred and fifty pounds—with a large round freckled face, usually grinning but just not at that moment.

"Mebbe you'd like to come back later when I've made a fresh pot," Red rumbled ominously. The dawdler hurriedly paid his bill and left.

A girl about my age took the empty stool. Not a raving beauty—we didn't get many raving beauties in Red's Rite Spot—but common-sense, June Allison pretty. She wore a white blouse with a Peter Pan collar, very little makeup, and no jewelry. Someone you could comfortably take home and introduce to your mother.

Six feet away, I stared admiringly at her. She noticed my interest and gave me a friendly smile. Overwhelmed, I waved at her with a large, soapy, oatmeal-encrusted pot in my hand.

She ordered the hamburger plate with string beans and cottage cheese. Obviously trying to watch her weight—that was a good sign. She began reading a thick book of Elizabethan sonnets while she ate. Probably a university student—that was also good. After Red cleared her plate, she continued to read while sipping her coffee—that was bad.

Red didn't discriminate between male and female coffee-dawdlers. He treated them all alike. When I saw him strolling toward her, wiping his hands on his apron, I rushed to her rescue.

Grabbing a slice of apple pie from the dessert case on the counter, I quickly thrust it in front of her.

"Care for some dessert? It's on the house." A large soap bubble from my hands deposited itself on top of the pie, giving it the appearance of pie a la mode with see-through ice cream.

"Why, thank you very much," she said in a soft voice. "That's very nice of you."

Red saw what I had done to keep his thumb out of her coffee. "That pie may be on *your* house, but it ain't on *mine*," he muttered in my ear. "It's gonna come outta your wages."

I didn't care.

*Red thrust a hairy thumb into the guy's coffee and
stirred slowly. "Coffee still warm?"*

Her name was Ruth Grimsby. Before she left, I invited her to dinner that night—at Red's.

In most circles, dinner at Red's Rite Spot wouldn't be considered a hot date, but making conversation in familiar surroundings was easier for me and my meal was free. Besides, I hadn't taken a girl out in a year and a half, and *any* kind of date was a hot date.

I had it all worked out. From five to six-thirty p.m. I would wash dishes. At six-thirty—just when the dinnertime crowd was easing up and there were stools available—Ruth and I could sit down and eat together.

Ruth arrived promptly. I quickly removed my apron and ushered her over to two empty stools.

"Shall I order for both of us?" I asked, attempting to introduce a small degree of elegance into the evening.

She smiled and nodded.

"Two grilled ham plates," I said authoritatively to Red. I was exercising my well-earned customer rights which took effect as soon as I was off duty and sitting on the other side of the counter. Red smirked, knowing that I was trying hard to impress this girl.

It was a magical meal. She listened attentively while I explained the rigors of engineering school and the importance of testing rockets at White Sands.

"Would you like some dessert?" I asked. "Today we have apple, cherry, and custard pie." She selected cherry.

"Two slices of cherry pie," I instructed Red.

Red smiled patronizingly. "Don't y'remember how ya liked the raisin pie from yesterday?" he reminded me. "I saved some 'specially for ya.'" He brought out a piece of raisin pie from under the counter and placed it in front of me. The unwritten employment contract at Red's Rite Spot specified that the only dessert you got with a free meal was yesterday's pie.

"Of course," I replied glibly. "How could I have forgotten?"

"Oh, look," Ruth cried, scanning the selections on the countertop jukebox. "You've got my favorite song!" She put a nickel in. The Ames Brothers began singing...

You,

    you,   *with*

        you...   *love*   *you,*

             in   *you,*

          I'm   *you...*

Suddenly, she blushed furiously. "I... uh... just like the *tune*. I don't pay any attention to the *words*."

Who's she kidding? My mind began feverishly plotting the next move.

"*From Here to Eternity* is playing over at the State Theater," I blurted out. "I hear it's pretty good. Wanna take in the early show?"

After the movie, we walked down State Street toward the Helen Newberry Residence where Ruth lived.

"I think the scene where Burt Lancaster and Deborah Kerr were lying in the sand with the waves washing over them was very romantic," Ruth said.

I should have agreed instantly, but my logical engineering mind took over. "I dunno... I bet wet sand would feel pretty clammy."

But it didn't alter her mood, and she put her arm through mine while we strolled down the street. As we neared Helen Newberry, Ruth asked "Would you like some Dentyne gum?"

A signal clearer than a beacon in the night. She wasn't offering me Spearmint or Juicy Fruit. It was Dentyne—the gum designed to ensure kissing-sweet breath.

We both popped Dentyne into our mouths and chewed furiously as we walked up to the dormitory door. I didn't have a chance to get rid of the gum because she suddenly turned and looked up at me expectantly, her gaze focussing on my lips. The Dentyne didn't get in the way at all.

Monday, July 13th, 1953
Ann Arbor

On the way out the door to my afternoon calculus class, I picked up my mail from the landlady's hallway table. As I hurried toward West Engineering, I opened a letter from home. As usual, the letter from my mother was full of advice on eating well, taking lots of vitamins, and dressing warmly—even in July. The old man had tucked in a note of his own.

Hello Jerry:

> *Two months ago there was still snow in the woods and now it's hot as hell. I hear you're taking out a nice girl. Don't get too serious right away. Marriage isn't all it's cracked up to be but maybe it's better when you got lots of money, so finish up your college. Your ma and I get along pretty good, though. Most of the time anyway.*

> *Pop*

At one o'clock Dale Ray and I took our seats in the Calculus II class in West Engineering, girding ourselves to do battle with integration of inverse trigonometric and hyperbolic forms, subject matter totally incompatible with the warm, summer air that was bathing Ann Arbor.

"Lookit that," Dale whispered to me. "Murphy's giving Highwater a drop slip to sign!"

"How can he do that?" I whispered back. "This's the fourth week—too late to drop. You sure it's a drop slip?"

"Of course it's a drop slip!" Dale hissed excitedly. "You ought'a know what a drop slip looks like by now."

That was true. After three gruelling weeks, we'd seen plenty of drop slips in this class. Eleven of the original eighteen students had dropped the course, leaving seven of us to the not-so-tender mercies of Professor Highwater.

In the spring semester, Calculus I had been no problem whatsoever—in fact I'd enjoyed it. But Calculus II—especially as taught by Horace Highwater—was a nightmare. Highwater's first blue book was on a par with a quiz on the theory of relativity. Each homework assignment took a day and a half to complete. My active social life—dating Ruth two or three nights a week—also wasn't enhancing my chances of getting through the course.

Dale grabbed my arm. "Look at that—I don't believe it—Highwater's signing Murphy's slip! He's still letting people drop his course! We gotta pick up drop slips right away and get Highwater to sign them!"

I really hated Calculus II but didn't want to get into the habit of dropping courses. "I dunno... I don't think it's a good idea. If we drop it, we still gotta take it next spring."

"Well, while you're thinking," Dale said in a low voice, "think about this... if we *flunk* this course, we *still* gotta take it next spring... except we'll have a much lower grade point average than if we drop it now."

That struck a nerve. Gradewise, I had improved in the spring semester, getting straight B's. No longer worried about just surviving at Michigan, I wanted to graduate with a good grade point average.

"You think Highwater'd *flunk* us?" I whispered.

"What'd you get on that first blue book?" Dale asked.

"D-minus."

"Me too. And do you remember what he called that blue book when he handed it back to us?"

"He said it was a warm-up exam."

"That's right," Dale said. "Do you think the final will be easier?"

"Uh... no."

"Well, then?" Dale said.

At four-thirty, we found Professor Highwater in his office and presented him with our Calculus II drop slips.

Highwater glanced at the slips with disdain. "Gentlemen," he snapped impatiently. "This is the fourth week of summer session classes. It's too late to drop the course."

That settled it as far as I was concerned. I started to edge toward the door, but Dale put a restraining hand on my arm.

"Sir... you let Murph... Mr. Murphy drop the course this afternoon before class."

Highwater leaned back in his wooden swivel chair, hooked his thumbs in his suspenders, and arrogantly gazed up at Dale through wire-rimmed reading glasses. "Mr. Ray, you would be well advised to apply yourself less to the business of your fellow students and more to your mathematics assignments, which—if I accurately recall your grade on the first exam— urgently need your attention."

"Thank you very much for your consideration, sir," I squeaked as I tried to peel Dale's fingers from my arm.

But Dale hung on, getting in the last word. "With all due respect, Dr. Highwater, we feel that this is unfair and Mr. Harju and I intend to seek higher council in this matter." He turned and abruptly left the office, leaving me standing there to wither under Highwater's glare. Gathering up what wits I had left, I bolted out the door.

I caught up with Dale in the hallway. "Nice going in there. Now we're *really* screwed. What's this '*Mr. Harju* and I intend to seek *higher council*'? *I'm* not seeking any higher council. I don't even know what higher council you're talking about."

"We're going to see Emmert," Dale said.

"Dean *Emmert*? You crazy?"

"Think about it... we're past the point of no return, old buddy. If we just knuckle under, ol' Highwater'll flunk us out of spite. But if we tell Emmert how many guys dropped out of Calculus II, I bet there'll be some action. And *you* gotta come with me to Emmert's office to back me up."

"Me? You want *me* to go to Emmert's office to rat on Highwater? Not in a million years!"

Dean Emmert glanced at his pocket watch and motioned Dale and me into his office. "I've got fifteen minutes before my next meeting, gentlemen, so please be brief. Now, what seems to be the problem?"

Dale related the events leading up to our being there—the arduous homework assignments and the exam that no mathematician, much less a sophomore engineering student, could have passed. From time to time, Emmert glanced over at me, and I dumbly nodded my head in agreement.

Dale concluded by saying that, one by one, two-thirds of the original class had dropped the course. That fact seemed to interest Emmert most.

"Twelve out of eighteen have dropped the course, you say?"

"That's right, sir," Dale said.

Emmert picked up the receiver of his telephone and dialed. "Dr. Highwater? Walter Emmert here. I wonder if you would come over to my office for a minute. Yes... right now, if you can. Thank you."

I suddenly had a strong urge to go to the men's room. Dale looked stricken as well, realizing that we were about to confront Highwater, right then and there in front of the dean.

Professor Highwater came in. His expression hardened when he saw Dale and me standing there. He immediately knew what the subject matter was.

Dean Emmert opened the discussion. "Dr. Highwater, these gentlemen seem to be distressed about the degree of difficulty of your Calculus II class. They claim that two-thirds of the class have already dropped the course. Is that correct?"

Highwater cleared his throat. "Dr. Emmert, I'm not certain what the exact figures are, but there *have* been a large number of drops from this class. This is not unusual during the summer. Students are making up courses that were failed in the spring and they find the fast-paced summer session even more rigorous." Then, Highwater glanced at Dale and me with a hint of a smile. "Also, I find that some students simply become lethargic in the warm weather."

That last comment was too much for Dale. "That's unfair, sir! Harju and I have worked our butts off in your course!"

Why did he keep bringing up my name every time he yelled at Highwater?

Emmert rapped on his desk. Gentlemen... gentlemen... I must leave for a meeting, so I'm going to render an immediate resolution in this matter. Mr. Ray and Mr. Harju—both of you are enrolled in the White Sands Co-op Program. That alone will delay your graduation date, and you can ill afford to postpone course work any longer than is absolutely necessary. I suggest that you buckle down and do your very best in Dr. Highwater's course. I'm sure he'll be more than fair with you." Emmert looked at his watch again and rose from his chair, indicating that the meeting was over.

As we walked out of Dean Emmert's office, Highwater grinned victoriously. We were doomed.

Thursday, August 13th, 1953
Ann Arbor

"**M**r. Harju... you have a telephone call."

I went downstairs and the landlady handed me the receiver.

"Hello?"

"Jerry, this is Dale. Come on over to the frat house and we'll cram for the final together."

"Thanks, but I don't think so. Cramming for finals with other guys never works for me—too much gabbing. If I'm gonna stand a chance with Highwater's final exam tomorrow, I gotta stay up and study all night—by myself."

"Lissen, I got something over here at the house that'll *guarantee* you'll pass his final. *Guarantee,* I tell ya."

"What's that?"

"Come on over an' you'll find out."

Dale opened up his fist. There were two little yellow pills in his hand.

"What're those?"

Dale grinned smugly. "I call 'em Einstein pills."

"What's in 'em?"

"Caffeine... same as coffee except a helluva lot stronger. You pop one of these babies and your IQ ratchets up about one hundred points. You can understand anything—even Highwater's Calculus II questions, I bet."

"You tried them?"

"Yep—last night, studying for the statics final. Didn't need a wink of sleep and I went through the textbook from cover to cover." He held his hand out. "Here, take one."

I shook my head. "Uh... I don't think so..."

"Think you're gonna pass Highwater's final, tomorrow morning?"

"If I'm lucky, I might squeak by with a D."

Dale held out the pills again. "On the other hand, if you *cream* the final, you might get a C in the course... maybe even a B! What've you got to lose?"

I grabbed a pill and swallowed it. "Probably won't work. To be on the safe side, you got any black coffee?"

"There's a whole urn in the dining room."

Two hours later I'd reviewed the first two chapters and correctly worked every problem in the Exercise sections.

"Y'know? This stuff doesn't seem nearly as hard as it was when we first started the course," I said to Dale.

Dale was busily calculating the surface area of a torus, deftly manipulating his slide rule with his left hand while he wrote down the answer with his right. "I was just thinking the same thing."

"I'm getting a little hungry. You got any food around?"

"If ya really want the pill to work, forget the food." Dale advised. "Food just makes you sleepy. Stick to coffee."

"I guess you're right," I said, pouring my fourth cup.

By midnight we had gone through polar coordinates, approximate integration, and improper integrals. A good start, but there was a great deal of material left.

"I have an idea," I said in a bright voice. "Since we still have a long way to go, I'll bet we could speed this whole thing up if we took another pill."

Dale was opening another pound of coffee for the urn. "I'll get two more."

We washed the pills down with black coffee. The effect was spectacular. By three a.m. we had absolutely annihilated all the exercises on indeterminate forms, Taylor's formula, and infinite series.

"Y'know? I may decide to become a mathematician," I remarked. "It'd be a pushover running off things like rocket-trajectory calculations. I could get another job on the side and pull down two paychecks. Maybe I'll just hang around here, grab a Ph.D. in math, and teach for awhile."

"You'd be bored doing nothing but math," Dale said. "Too easy. I was thinking... if we get A's in the Calc II final this morning—and we can do that easy—Highwater's got to give us *at least* a B in the course. Isn't that right?"

"Yup," I agreed. "I know he's mad at us, but he can't ignore talent."

Partial derivatives and multiple integrals were more challenging, but nothing we couldn't handle. By five a.m. we had gone through all of the material covered in the course.

"There's still another chapter in the book—differential equations," Dale exclaimed. His voice had taken on a curiously high pitch, like a 45 rpm record being played at 78.

"Dale, Highwater didn't even *cover* differential equations. We don't have to do that."

"So what?" Dale cried. "We gotta take differential equations next spring anyhow, so why not bone up on it now?"

"Naw," I said. "We're done. I think I'll catch a few hours sleep. Wake me up when it's time to go for the final."

Dale was busily tearing into differential equations as I went to sleep on the fraternity-house hallway sofa.

Friday, August 14th, 1953
Ann Arbor

I was being shaken violently but couldn't see what was doing it because some prankster had glued my eyelids shut. I finally got my eyes open, but the bright light blinded me so badly I had to shut them again. I had a horrible headache. My body was still being jolted about.

I opened my eyes just a slit. A huge hand, attached to a fifty-yard arm, was shaking my shoulder. A very large face—one I knew but couldn't remember—was talking at me.

"Hey, Jer... snap out of it. It's seven-thirty. Time to go."

The words banged against my ear drums, greatly intensifying the headache. My legs were swung to the floor, dangerously sloshing the toxic contents of my stomach. My bladder, ballooned to bursting, was letting me know that I'd better find a bathroom—fast.

I looked again at the person shaking me. "Dale... is that you?" I tried to say, but all that came out was a gravely croak. There wasn't a single molecule of saliva in my mouth.

"C'mon," Dale urged. "We gotta get down to West Engineering."

"Why?"

"Why? For the Calculus II final, that's why."

Calculus II—the words were familiar, but I couldn't remember exactly what they meant.

"Dale, where's the toilet?"

He pointed to a door across the foyer and I made a beeline for it.

Dale finally hustled me out of the house and we headed down Washtenaw Avenue toward the campus. Every footstep jarred my brain.

"Here's an easy one for ya," Dale chirped. "What's the integral of the hyperbolic secant squared?"

"What?"

"Don't know? It's the hyperbolic tangent plus a constant. You're in trouble if you can't answer a simple one like that."

It was coming back to me—the all-night cramming, the coffee, the caffeine pills.

The caffeine had Dale hitting on all cylinders. Every so often he would involuntarily take jerky little dance steps. One maneuver took him off the curb and into the street. An oncoming driver laid on the horn, causing me to jump several feet in the air.

"You're pretty jittery this morning," Dale said, slapping himself to control a tic in his right cheek. "You shouldn't've gone to sleep. It takes the edge off the Einstein pills."

"*Now* you tell me!"

"Here's another one... define the Hyperharmonic Series using an exponent k."

I didn't know the difference between a Hyperharmonic Series and a harmonica. Last night, without a moment's hesitation, I had been spitting out answers to complex calculus problems. This morning I couldn't even *spell* calculus.

Not waiting for an answer, Dale rattled off another problem. "I bet'cha Highwater'll ask this one... describe the integral test for convergence and divergence."

"Dale, just shut the hell up."

But Dale wasn't about to quit. Spotting two women coming out of one of the sorority houses, he ran up to them. "Ya wanna know what the fundamental theorem for double integrals is?" he shouted.

"Get lost, creep, or we'll call the police," one of them snarled.

I grabbed Dale by the arm and we proceeded on to West Engineering. We got to the classroom just as Professor Highwater was passing out the final exam. I sat down and looked at the first problem. It was totally incomprehensible. Panicked, I looked at the second problem. And the third. I finally screwed up my courage and did what I had to do. I got up, went down the hall to the men's room, and threw up.

I sat up in bed with a start. Someone was calling my name. The clock on the dresser said four-thirty and light was coming in the window, so it must have been afternoon and not early morning. After the disastrous Calculus II final, I had come back to the room and passed out on the bed.

The landlady was calling from the stairwell. "You have a telephone call."

I stumbled down the stairs, trying to shake the cobwebs out of my head as I picked up the receiver. "Hello."

"Jer... this is Sternitzky." Letch Sternitzky, my friend from the spring semester drafting class had also attended summer session. "How'd you do on your finals?"

"Okay on the engineering statics, not so good on calculus." I explained what had happened at Dale's frat house and the consequences at Highwater's final exam. "I felt a little better after barfing and went back in the classroom and managed to work a few of the problems. I'm just hoping for a D in the course."

"Well, that's water under the bridge. Tonight's your last night in town, isn't it?"

"Yeah. I'm leaving for New Mexico in the morning."

"You taking your girl out tonight?"

"Yeah. Ruth and I are probably just gonna get a bite to eat and take in a movie—maybe *Stalag 17* at the Michigan Theater."

"*Stalag 17?*" Letch exclaimed incredulously. "The last night with your girl and you're taking her to a *war* movie? Not too classy. Wanna hear a better idea?"

"What's that?"

"I been taking care of somebody's house while they're on summer vacation. An engineering prof and his family who live out on Huron River Drive. Pretty fancy place. I figure we could double date, bring the girls out here to the house, and listen to some music."

"The owner lets you bring people over?"

"They're outta town till next week. Who's to know?"

"Is that really a TV set?" I asked. I had no idea TV screens were made that big.

"Yep, a twenty-one-incher," Letch declared proudly. "But it's more than that. It's a Sylvania Monticello console combo. TV... AM-FM radio... 3-speed phono... the works."

"Look at this rug," Ruth exclaimed. "It goes all the way to the walls."

Ruth and I and Letch and his date Gail had just entered the quietly elegant living room where Letch was house-sitting for the summer. Letch went to the console and turned on the TV. Half a minute later, the twenty-one-inch screen blazed to life. A gigantic Ed Sullivan had just introduced a team of seals decked out in New York Knicks uniforms. We all watched intently as the seals cleverly passed a basketball from nose to nose.

A commercial came on, and Letch turned the TV off and flipped on the phonograph. "Why don't we put some music on instead?" He stacked several long-playing records onto the automatic turntable. "Ebb Tide" drifted across the room.

"Anybody care for a little drink?" Letch asked from a small bar against the wall. He had produced a tall frosty glass filled with ice cubes clinking together invitingly.

"Whatever you're having," Gail said provocatively. Letch grinned and brought up a large bottle of rum from below the bar.

"Do you have any Coca-Cola?" Ruth asked.

"Sure, but why don't you let me put a touch of rum in it. Makes a great drink... can't even taste the rum. After all, we gotta celebrate getting through summer session, don't we?"

"Just a tiny bit then," Ruth said tentatively.

"I'll take the same," I said.

Letch poured a large shot of rum and some Coke into each of the four glasses and passed the drinks around. He motioned to the Sylvania. "If you really wanna appreciate the fidelity of this sound system, you gotta get down next to the speakers... right here on the floor."

We all sat down on the carpet in front of the huge console and sipped our drinks. "Getting to Know You" drifted softly out of the speakers. I put my arm around Ruth, and she leaned her head back onto my shoulder. The memory of the Calculus II final began to fade.

Another record slid down the automatic spindle onto the turntable, but for awhile no sound came from the speakers. Then, a soft syncopated beat emerged, followed by a haunting melody played by a single oboe. It was Ravel's "Bolero." Never having heard it before, I had no idea that it was one of the most seductive pieces of music ever written.

Other instruments joined in, supporting the oboe in repeating the melody. The volume grew and the beat became more restless. By now we had finished our drinks and all four of us were lying on the carpet, absorbed with the hypnotic melody. I leaned over Ruth. We looked into each other's eyes and kissed. Not an ordinary kiss but soft and lingering. It had the faintly exotic essence of rum and Dentyne chewing gum.

I didn't have to look up to know what was going on with Letch and Gail. I could hear the heavy breathing.

The melody, now led by violins, kept repeating, not monotonously, but continually inching upward in volume and tempo, promising the listener further exotic pleasures.

Ruth, eyes closed, was lying on her back on the carpet. We kissed again, longer, harder, with more urgency. I came up for air, but she put her arms around my neck and pulled me back down again. As we kissed, I opened my eyes, briefly glancing at the beige carpet. It had become sand on an Oahu beach, and the music was warm seawater washing over our bodies. I was Burt Lancaster, and Ruth was Deborah Kerr.

Led by throbbing trumpets, "Bolero" engulfed the room, converging on some unknown but inevitable destination. I placed my hand on Ruth's breast.

She sat bolt upright on the carpet.

"*WHAT* DO YOU THINK YOU'RE DOING?"

Ruth scrambled to her feet. "I see... you thought you could pour a little rum in me, take advantage—here on the rug of all places—and then run off to New Mexico for the winter. Well, you got another think coming, buster. C'mon, Gail. Let's go."

Letch and Gail, in the midst of an advanced stage of unbuttoning, sat up. Feeling obligated to side with Ruth, Gail buttoned up and got to her feet.

The front door slammed shut just as "Bolero" reached its climactic ending.

"Why're you taking *that* with you?" Letch asked sarcastically as I put Ruth's high-school-graduation picture into my suitcase. It was almost midnight. After Ruth and Gail abruptly left us, Letch had come back to my room with me to keep me company while I finished packing. Actually, Letch wanted someone to keep *him* company, since he had been all geared up for a party and the sudden departure of the girls had cheated him out of it. To help things along he'd brought along a sackful of refreshments.

"Oh... I dunno," I mumbled dejectedly. "She may calm down in a few days. When I get to White Sands I'll write her a letter and apologize."

Letch snorted in disgust as he extracted a bottle of liquor from the sack. "Apologize? For *what*? Touching one of her boobs? Not even *that* fer chrissake—just her blouse. Doesn't she know this's the 1950's?" He broke the seal on the liquor bottle. "You got any glasses around here?"

I gave him the water glass I used for brushing my teeth. "What *is* that stuff?"

Letch poured four inches of clear liquor into the glass. "Gin." He handed it to me.

I'd never had gin, but I needed something to ease the pain of my shattered romance. I took a gulp. It tasted terrible, but it was, after all, strictly medicinal.

Next, Letch produced a cardboard box from the sack. It contained an angel food cake wrapped in waxed paper. "From my mother," he explained. "She sent it weeks ago. I gotta be able to tell her I ate it."

We sat for awhile eating angel food cake and washing it down with gin. The cake was stale and the gin tasted like turpentine—not much of a combination, but after a few rounds it didn't seem quite so bad.

Letch grew philosophical as we got deeper into the gin. "Y'know? You're probably better off without that prude. Now you can play the field. I sure wish she hadn't dragged Gail off, though," he muttered. "One more round of 'Bolero' would've done the job. It was money in the bank."

"Whaddaya mean?" My tongue was getting somewhat thick.

"I gotta spell it out for ya?" He pulled out his wallet and produced a prophylactic. "I was all prepared, too."

"Y'mean... you were gonna go to the bedroom?"

"Of course. She probably would'a objected to the rug. Too public."

I took a big gulp of gin. "And what was *I* supposed to do while you were... ?"

"You serious? The house's got *four* bedrooms. You could'a taken your pick."

"Jeez, is that what you had in mind all along?"

"Naturally," Letch said. "Didn't you?"

I took another drink of gin. I was beginning to realize how naive I was. Sex hadn't occurred to me at all. I simply thought that it was going to be a nice romantic evening listening to music, perhaps a little cuddling and a kiss or two.

"I don't think I'll *ever* get a girl into the sack," I said, passing the gin glass back to Letch. "I haven't got the knack for it."

Letch paused with the glass halfway up to his lips. "Wait a minute... wait a minute. Y'mean t'tell me that you *never* had a girl?"

Right then I knew I was drunk because this was closely guarded information, but the gin was prompting me to air it out. I shook my head.

"Gawdamn," Letch exclaimed. "How old're you?"

"Just twenty," I said defensively. "But my birthday was only in April, so I'll be twenty for quite awhile yet."

"Twenty?" cried Letch taking a mouthful of gin and passing the glass back to me. "Sheet... you're almost old enough to *drink*. Y'gotta lose your virginity right away."

"Whyizzat?" I slurred.

"Don't y'know nothin'? Physically, these're your best years for sex. Once you get into your mid twenties, it's all downhill, until you reach forty, and then you won't be doing it at *all* 'cause y'won't be able to get it up."

Letch smiled craftily. "But from what you told me, there's a lotta 'spicy tamales' down there in old Mexico, am I right?"

"Somma 'em are li'l *too* spicy," I said, thinking of the B-girls in the Juarez nightclubs who thought nothing of grabbing your crotch and twisting until you bought them a drink.

"Then it should be no problem," Letch said. "And think about this... if you patch it up with Ruth, she'll thank you. Women appreciate experienced men."

I took a nervous pull on the gin, emptying the glass. "You're right. I'll take care of it right away."

Saturday, August 15th, 1953
Ann Arbor

It was the second morning in a row that I found myself throwing up into a toilet bowl, and I hoped this wasn't going to become a habit. The mixture of gin and angel food cake was even worse coming up than it had been going down. I settled down on the tiled floor, arms wrapped around the cold porcelain, to indulge my stomach with a few remaining spasms. My landlady appeared at the door.

"Goodness... are you not feeling well?"

I shook my head but not too forcefully since it might fall into the bowl.

"There's a group of young men waiting for you in a car at the curb," she said.

I lurched to my feet and wobbled into the room to get my suitcase. I had somehow managed to finish packing, although one of my shirts had attempted an escape—a sleeve dangling out of the closed suitcase.

Jim Fordham, Bob Kruger, Jack Sherman, Dale Ray, and Niles Meeker were waiting in Fordham's brand-new '53 Plymouth. This time we'd be travelling down to White Sands in style.

"Jeesus... you look like hell," Fordham remarked.

"Before we get going, take me over to Red's Rite Spot," I croaked as I got into the car. "I gotta pick up a week's pay."

"Jeesus... you look like hell," Red said as he handed me my wages. Without asking, he put a steaming cup of black coffee down on the counter in front of me. "Wanna piece of apple pie? Made this morning... no charge."

I was so overwhelmed by Red's generosity that I temporarily forgot the delicate condition of my stomach and began wolfing down the pie. My thoughts turned to Ruth. I put one last nickel in the jukebox. The Ames Brothers burst into song.

You,
    you,   *with*
        you...   *love*   *you,*
                in   *you,*
      I'm   *you...*

"That's one thing I ain't gonna miss after you leave," Red commented dryly. "Havin' to listen to that damned song all day."

Extracurricular Education

White Sands Proving Ground
August 1953 - January 1954

Monday, August 17th, 1953
White Sands Proving Ground

Jim Fordham didn't want his new Plymouth driven over fifty miles an hour—after all, the engine needed to be broken in properly. But whenever he was asleep the rest of us would covertly push the Plymouth up to seventy. We got to White Sands in two days, just in time to attend another Lester Tinley orientation meeting.

While we were away, Tinley had been promoted to first lieutenant. His stance was even more ramrod straight. His uniform had sharper creases. His pimples were expertly covered with Clearasil.

"Welcome back to White Sands Proving Ground," he said. "Beginning this tour of duty, your Civil Service rank will be GS-3, with a salary increase to one dollar and thirty-five cents an hour."

This was exciting news. There would be an extra eight dollars—minus taxes, of course—in my paycheck every two weeks.

"GS-3's are eligible—for a five-dollar annual fee—to join the Officers' Club. As members, you are entitled to all the privileges afforded to officers of the United States Army." Tinley waited impatiently for our response.

"Gentlemen, don't you understand? You'll no longer have to eat at the Enlisted Men's Mess."

It suddenly dawned on us—no more World War II powdered scrambled eggs, creamed chipped beef on toast, filet of Spam, or gravy ice cream sundaes. We gave Tinley a round of applause.

Tinley droned on about recent organizational changes at White Sands and newly instituted military rules and regulations that would be imposed on us. We picked up our badges at Security. The Quonset hut where we lived last year had been commandeered by the Corps of Engineers for storing rocket debris recovered from the range, so we were given new quarters in a converted wooden barracks down the street. This new Bachelor Officers' Quarters (BOQ) was a big improvement. The rooms were larger, the air coolers didn't vibrate the wooden building as they did the metal Quonset hut, and the olive-drab furniture was better styled.

After settling in, we eagerly took off for lunch at the Officers' Club. The hot sun was oppressive, like a heavy woolen blanket.

As we passed the fire station, the siren on the roof went off. Two fire engines roared out and tore off down the straight six-mile stretch of road to the launch area. At the far end, a rising plume of smoke shimmered in the heat waves.

"Mishap out at the blockhouse," Tinley observed matter-of-factly. "Third time this month."

A grim reminder that White Sands Proving Ground was not a college campus.

The outside of the Officers' Club resembled every other bare-bones, wooden building on the base, but the inside was vastly different. The dining room was furnished with beige, wall-to-wall carpeting and drapes, and the tables had starched white tablecloths, cloth napkins, and real plates. It was a far cry from the austere, prison-like dining-hall at the Enlisted Men's Mess.

"Seven for lunch," Tinley commanded a white-coated waiter with a GI haircut who nodded obediently and escorted us over to a large table.

"There is only one entree each day," Tinley explained. "Today it's American-style sauteed goulash."

I'd never heard of it, but whatever it was, it sounded good. We hadn't eaten a thing other than a few vending-machine candy bars during an early morning gas stop in Truth or Consequences, New Mexico. We were starved.

The food quickly arrived and we all dug in.

Sherman savored a mouthful. "This is *hash!*" he exclaimed.

"Not only that... it's *mess-hall* hash," someone added.

The covered basket meant for hot rolls was filled with the same pasty, sliced white bread that loomed in tall stacks at the mess hall.

"There's only one kitchen on base," Tinley admitted, "over at the Enlisted Men's Mess."

I didn't participate in the heated discussion that followed. The hash tasted better here than over at the mess hall—I just shovelled it in.

After lunch I reported for work at the Climatic Test Lab.

Bob Flint was glad to see me. "We're just now starting the design of the Viking thermal jacket. I've got a drafting table waiting for you."

I glanced around the lab, crammed with even more equipment than before. "Where?"

"We've expanded," Flint said proudly. "Come with me."

The temperature inside the large assembly building next door was stifling because its air coolers weren't operating. The building—previously used to assemble and test German V-2's—was now only a repository for large stacks of rocket parts, test equipment, and miscellaneous junk.

But off in one corner were two drafting tables underneath a hand-painted sign.

CLIMATIC TESTING LABORATORY—DESIGN SECTION

A GI in a sweat-stained khaki T-shirt—a stripe sewn on each shoulder—hunched over one of the tables. Flint introduced me to Joe Raven, an engineering grad from Georgia Tech, presently suffering the indignities of life as a private first class. The army had loaned him to the Climatic Testing Lab to work on the Viking job. I was to be his assistant.

With his horn-rimmed glasses, Raven could have passed for a young college professor—from the neck up. From the neck down he looked like any other GI.

"You know anything about this job we're gonna work on?" Raven inquired.

"Uh... no."

"Grab a stool and I'll fill you in."

After Flint left, Raven quickly began sketching on a large piece of paper on his drafting board. "This's the Viking missile... about the same size as the V-2." It was a lousy drawing of a rocket, but I nodded obligingly.

He continued. "You and I are gonna design a thermal cover to encase the rocket... like this." Raven drew a jello-like blob over his questionable-looking rocket. "A big hollow cylinder made out of aluminum, wood, and insulation. Like a giant thermos bottle, except it's put together and taken apart in sections. During a test, hot or cold air is pumped into it."

He began quizzing me about my engineering background. "Ever work on a design job like this before?"

"No."

"Ever run heat-flow calculations?"

"No."

"Static load analysis?"

"No."

He shook his head sadly. "Damn, what *can* you do?"

Spotting his sly, needling grin, I jabbed a finger at his sketches. "I can *draw* better than that."

Wednesday, August 26th, 1953
White Sands Proving Ground

As soon as I had arrived at White Sands, I'd written to Ruth. The letter was a masterpiece of grovelling, cries of loneliness, and declarations of undying love.

Today I received a reply:

Dear Jerry,

How nice to hear from you. It must be very hot down there in the desert. I imagine it's dry though. The weather has been muggy here with many thunderstorms which still frighten me quite a lot.

As you can see from the return address, I am back home in Detroit with my parents until school starts in September. Every morning I put on my swimming suit and go out in the backyard to work on my suntan, but most of the time the weather has been too cloudy.

Please write again. I always like to get mail.

Very truly yours,
Ruth

I didn't understand this. How could my beautiful letter trigger a Michigan weather report? Was she still mad at me for putting a hand on her breast? But she *did* answer my letter and ask me to write again. Perhaps I'd been reduced to the status of a neuter pen pal—someone to exchange pleasantries with until the right man came along.

But why wasn't *I* the right man?

The words of Letch Sternitzky echoed in my brain. *Women appreciate experienced men.*

I knew what had to be done and where to do it.

Thursday, August 27th, 1953
White Sands Proving Ground

After two weeks of sweating side by side at our drafting tables in the corner of the old missile assembly building, Joe Raven and I had become pretty good friends. This was fortunate because I desperately needed the advice of an older man.

As Raven and I put away our T-squares and triangles for the day, I took the plunge.

"Joe, you go to Juarez much?"

"Well, I get down there sometimes. Juarez isn't Gay Par-ee, but it beats staring at forty-seven other dogfaces in the barracks every night."

"Well... y'see, I kind'a need... no—wait a minute... I been thinking I might..."

"You wanna go to a cathouse, right?"

My face got hot. "Well... yeah... but not one of those sleazy joints. I want something better. You know any good places?"

"Irma's"

"What?"

"You wanna go to Irma's. The only decent place in Juarez. Clean. Women aren't bad-looking either."

"Uh... okay... does it cost much?"

Raven grinned mysteriously. "Not if I come with you."

"Why is that?"

Raven didn't answer the question. "You going down there tonight?"

I got frightened. "Tonight? Oh, no... I was thinking maybe this week-end... or even September sometime. No rush."

"Weekends are bad—too crowded. Another thing—payday is next Tuesday. All the GI's are broke right now. Tonight would be perfect."

My old man always said, "If you got somethin' scary to do, it don't get any better with age."

"Tonight, huh? Well... okay... why not?"

"Let me get cleaned up and get a pass," Raven said. "I'll see you at the bus stop at six o'clock."

Avenida Juarez was crowded with the usual foot traffic—tourists shopping for a deal and GI's shopping for a drink.

Raven stopped at the first taxi parked at the curb. "Irma's," he said to the driver.

The driver nodded, and we got in the taxi. With a clash of gears, we took off in a dense cloud of blue exhaust. The driver turned onto a dark, dirt-road side street and proceeded into a part of Juarez I'd never seen before.

Raven looked around, leaned forward over the front seat, and spoke in rapid Spanish to the driver. The driver meekly mumbled something and made a left turn.

Raven sat back and said to me, "Guy was taking us somewhere else—probably a house run by his brother-in-law. Had to let him know I knew the way to Irma's."

"You speak Spanish?"

"Of course. When I'm at home, my mother calls me Jose, not Joe."

"I thought you were American—from the south somewhere."

Raven laughed. "You think I'd be wearing khaki underwear if I wasn't American? Born in San Antonio, Texas. But my parents came from Monterrey, Mexico. My father changed his name from Rivera to Raven. Said it was easier to get a job with an Anglo-sounding name."

The taxi stopped at a one-story adobe building on a hill. There were no signs or lights at the entrance, and no light showed from the windows. It looked deserted.

"Are they open?" I asked.

"They're open," said Raven, getting out of the taxi.

The driver wanted to come in with us, but Raven again spoke to him in Spanish. Judging from the gestures, Raven told him to stay in the car and wait for us.

We opened the door and were bathed with warm light and lively music from a large well-decorated room with a colorful tiled floor. An ornate, hand-carved wooden bar dominated the far wall. A Mexican love song—laced with plenty of "mi corazon" (my heart)—was playing on a jukebox.

But the ladies standing at the bar weren't after our corazones. Expressionless, hard-edged faces, heavy with makeup, surveyed us with predatory interest. Their hands—holding lit cigarettes—were armed with lethally sharp, bright red fingernails. All of the women were poured into tight, glittery dresses, breasts jutting out like rocket nose cones.

I'd encountered B-girls in the downtown Juarez clubs. Their job was simple—if you bought them a drink, they got a percentage from the management and in return you got female company and short-term license to place a hand on a thigh or—if you were daring—perhaps a breast.

But this was *the real thing*—strictly major league. Looking at the women, my mind raced to the edge of panic imagining what might happen to me if any one of them got me alone in a room.

"Which one do *you* like?" I asked Raven in a squeaky voice.

"*Me?* I just came down here to help *you* out. I don't have any money. Payday is next week... remember?"

We took a table near the bar and sat down. The bartender came over for a drink order.

"Two cervezas, please, señor," Raven told him. He was speaking English. In fact, he fractured "cervezas" and "senor" like someone who didn't know Spanish.

The bartender brought the beer. Two of the women immediately strutted toward us, spike heels clicking rhythmically on the tiled floor.

Raven quickly leaned over and said, "Let me do the talking." That was fine with me. I was scared silly.

"Choo wan us to seet weeth you?" asked one of the women, exhaling a stream of smoke from one of those gawdawful sweet-smelling Mexican cigarettes.

Raven gave her a wide, bland smile. "Why, thank you very much, but give us a few more minutes to enjoy your wonderful Mexican beer." The woman muttered something in Spanish to the other, and they both walked back to the bar.

"That wasn't very nice," Raven said. "She called me a lily-livered douche bag." He leaned over and spoke earnestly. "You *never* select the ones standing at the bar—they're not the best. Wait and see who comes out from the back."

He was right. A few minutes later a girl appeared from a back room with a guy. She was totally different—very good-looking with a soft, gentle face. By far the youngest in the room.

"*That* one," I exclaimed, excitedly pointing at the girl.

"Don't do that," Raven whispered hoarsely, pushing my hand down. "It drives up the price. I'll invite her over and get the ball rolling. Then it's up to you."

Raven motioned the girl over to our table and began talking in slow English. "My friend here wants to know how much will it cost... for the pleasure of your company."

The girl wasn't sure she understood the multi-syllable words. "How mooch?" she said, pointing to herself.

Raven nodded.

She told us the price.

I was shocked. I didn't know losing my virginity would be so expensive. I leaned over to Raven and whispered, "I don't have that much money. We'd better leave."

Raven looked at me like I'd lost my marbles. "Haven't you ever been shopping in Mexico? The first price is always sky high. This is the girl you want, right?"

I nodded.

"Then, tell her it's too much. Go ahead... tell her."

I took a big gulp of beer. "Uh... gee, I'm sorry, but it's too much money," I said to her.

"Too mooch?" she asked.

"Yes."

The girl went back to the bar and spoke to one of the older women who seemed to be in charge. Raven leaned back in his chair, an ear cocked toward the pair. The two women chattered in Spanish.

Raven bent forward and translated for me. "The older dame said she hates the end of the month. Everybody's broke before payday. She told the young one to give you the virgin story and if that doesn't work, to knock a few dollars off since things are so slow tonight."

The girl came back and repeated her original price. "Thees ees good price for me. Las' week I was virgeen." She gave me a very sad look with big brown doe eyes.

The jukebox switched from Mexican love songs to "Almost Like Being in Love."

Raven signalled to me with a jerk of his head and got up, pretending he was getting ready to leave. I followed suit. Seeing this, the girl immediately lowered the price. I was beginning to see the logic in having Raven along as my interpreter and financial advisor.

I sat back down and took another large pull on my beer. Feeling braver and warming up to the bargaining, I said to her, "Still too much money."

"Steel too mooch?" she asked with widened eyes. I nodded. She shook her head and meekly trotted off to the bar, speaking again to the older woman.

This time Raven didn't have to lean back to overhear the conversation in Spanish because it got considerably louder, punctuated with obscene gestures by the head woman.

He translated. "The old one called you a toad-sucking tightwad and wants to throw us both out, but the young one thinks you're kind of cute—like a puppy dog—and probably a virgin. She hasn't had a virgin in awhile and would like to make a deal. The other one finally said okay; she could lower the price one more time, but that's it."

As the girl headed back toward our table Raven said, "Now it's up to you, buddy."

The jukebox began playing "How Much is That Doggie in the Window?"

Before I knew what was happening, it was over. I couldn't believe how quick it was. For years I'd dreamt of this moment: the slow removal of clothing; the prolonged, moist kisses; and the delicate caresses and rapid breathing. It wasn't like that at all.

When I returned to the barroom, Raven was still nursing the same drink. I expected him to ask me how it was, but he apparently knew how it was and didn't say a word. I sat down, still in shock, and began morosely sipping the remainder of my beer. It was still cold.

Moments later, the girl appeared from the back, handed the head woman my money and came to our table.

"You buy me dreenk?" she asked, smiling at me coyly.

It would have been the gentlemanly thing to do, but the woman at the bar now had all my money. "I think we gotta be going," I told her.

She laughed, playing with a three-by-five punch card—one like newspaper delivery boys used to keep track of payments. Hers had over a hundred holes in it.

"What's that?" I asked, getting up from the table.

"One man, one poonch," she said. "Ees how I get paid."

I gaped at all the punched holes, amazed. "I thought you said you were a virgin last week," I said.

She laughed again. "Oh yass, but thees card is for thees week *only*."

The jukebox began playing "Your Cheatin' Heart."

Thursday, December 24th, 1953
White Sands Launch Area

Tonight while most people were at home wrapping and opening presents, drinking eggnog, and generally having a festive time, my butt was out at the blockhouse, crammed into an army van loaded with instrumentation. I was babysitting a hot missile and toasting the Yuletide season with not-so-hot thermos-bottle coffee.

Our lab was running a one-hundred-hour heat test on an Honest John, a twenty-seven-foot tactical-strike missile designed for use on ground targets behind the Iron Curtain. For mobility, the missile was launched from a rail on the rear of an army truck. The missile had an ominous bulging nose to house an atomic warhead. Before the test, Flint had assured his troops that the warhead wasn't included in our test missile, since no one was particularly anxious to sit around cooking an atomic bomb.

Our van was parked next to the blockhouse near the huge truck with an Honest John mounted on its back. Like last year's Nike test, the missile was sealed in a canvas-covered blanket connected by air ducts to our trailer-mounted Field Refrigeration Unit. The unit had been modified by installing a bank of electrical heaters in the dry ice compartment to blow hot air instead of cold. Flint renamed it the Field All Temperature Unit—the FAT box, for short.

For three days we had been heating the Honest John with one-hundred-and-forty-degree air. It needed to be launched hot to determine if the rocket subsystems would operate at that temperature. Launch was the day after Christmas, and whatever reasons the army brass had for running the test over the holidays had not filtered down to us peons at the test site.

Around midnight, after recording temperatures into the log book, I began a small-scale Christmas celebration. For atmosphere I turned on the van radio—permanently locked onto the zillion-watt, manure-kicking, country station coming out of Del Rio, Texas. Tonight they were actually playing Christmas carols—most of them by Gene Autry, naturally.

I opened the Christmas card and gift from my parents. Since I was a kid, I had always opened my presents the first thing on Christmas morning, and I wasn't about to let a tactical-strike missile interfere with this time-honored tradition.

The card was one of those big, fancy "To Our Son At Christmas" cards that my mother always bought—loaded with elegant prose describing my outstanding qualities as a son. A note from the old man was enclosed.

Hello Jerry:

So you got a raise in pay. Your ma and I figured out that you get more than two hundred and thirty dollars a month now. That's more than I made in a year when I was your age. The big money might not last, so don't let it go to your head. Keep up with your schooling.

It'll be a real white Christmas here. About two feet of snow on the ground now. I bet you don't miss snow shovelling.

> *Merry Christmas*
> *Pop*

I'd have given *anything* to be back in Upper Michigan shovelling snow tonight.

Carefully removing the red-and-green gift wrapping from my lone present, I opened the small box.

It was a Bulova pocket watch.

A pocket watch! Nobody used pocket watches anymore. Not quite accurate—my old man was a dedicated pocket-watch owner and would be till the day he died.

But *I* certainly didn't have any use for one. I'd just bought a new wristwatch at the PX—a jazzy waterproof, dustproof Timex Marlin with a sweep second hand and a radiolite dial that glowed in the dark.

I jammed the Bulova into my lunch pail. It was Christmas morning, and I was lonely and feeling sorry for myself.

Headlights flashed across the dusty van window, tires screeched, and a pickup truck door slammed. Thank gawd—my midnight relief was here. I was ready to crawl into bed and forget about Christmas.

The van door crashed open. Bill Longhorse stumbled in—dead drunk.

Longhorse was a co-op student at New Mexico A&M who had just started working for Flint. All I knew about him was that he was a full-blooded Apache Indian from someplace in Arizona.

"Y'know they sell beer over at the NCO club for fifteen cents a can?" he exclaimed, filling the van with beer fumes. "Fer a buck, y'kin get a purty good start on a toot over there!" That was the most he'd said to me since we met.

"How did you get served at the NCO club?"

"Whaddaya mean by that crack?" Longhorse asked suspiciously.

"I mean... didn't they ask you for I.D.—make sure you're over twenty-one?"

He calmed down a bit. "Oh... I thought you meant 'cause I'm an Indian." Then his voice rose again. "I'm twenty-two, an' I kin drink wherever th'hell I want."

I sensed trouble. "Are you working graveyard tonight?"

He stared owlishly around the van, trying to focus his eyes. "Yeah. Go home'n open up yer Christmas presents. I'll take 'er from here."

"Why don't you have a cup of my coffee?" I suggested, opening up the thermos bottle.

Longhorse snorted. "And spoil a perfectly good Christmas Eve blast? No, thanks."

"Look, you've had a few beers and you'll get sleepy just sitting here. It's going to be a long night and the coffee helps. I've been drinking a lot of it."

For a long moment we just stared at each other. I must have made sense because he blinked blearily and nodded. I quickly poured him a cup of coffee before he changed his mind.

He noisily slurped the coffee and put the empty cup down on top of a temperature recorder. I grabbed it up to give him a refill.

The thermos was dry.

Longhorse thought it was uproariously funny that I'd run out of coffee. "No more? Hah! If y'think one li'l cup a coffee'll sober *me* up, y'don't know much." He belligerently stood inside the van door, swaying from side to side. Steadying himself with a hand on top of one of the recorders, his large frame completely blocked the narrow aisle.

This was very dicey. If I left him here, he'd surely fall asleep. Although there wasn't *that* much to do, the FAT unit fan louvers *did* have to be adjusted periodically, because the missile temperatures tended to drift upward from time to time, and I didn't want to think about two thousand pounds of Honest John solid propellant becoming overheated. If I told him to go home because he was too drunk to work, he'd probably tear my head off. I glanced briefly at the field phone hanging from a peg on the van wall, thinking about calling Flint. If I did that, Longhorse would get fired. The only remaining option was to hang around and talk him sober.

I got up from the chair in front of the van's tiny table where we kept the log book and motioned for him to sit down. He slumped onto the seat.

It only took a few minutes to explain what I had been doing, but Longhorse was already drifting into sullen silence—a precursor to sleep. I kept talking.

"I'm wide awake from all the coffee, and there isn't anyplace to go this time of night. Mind if I stay here and keep you company for awhile?"

"Suit yourself," he muttered.

"How come you didn't go home for Christmas?"

Longhorse laughed bitterly. "Go home for Christmas," he said mockingly. "You know where I live?"

I shook my head.

"An Indian reservation—in a wood shack—no plumbing. We get water from a government tanker truck comes by twice a week. We crap in a outhouse. When it rains, the roof leaks like hell. When the wind blows, the dust comes in through the cracks in the walls like there wuzn't any walls at all. Got two younger brothers and one sister—they sleep on mattresses on the living room floor." Longhorse, more alert now, looked at me defiantly. "Why don't I go home for Christmas? One of my brothers already got my mattress, that's why."

I was shocked, then curious. "Where did you go to school?"

"There's a small school with missionary teachers—never enough books—sometimes they even hafta scramble t'get pencils and paper. Only has five grades. If ya wanna go further—an' most of 'em don't bother—then ya gotta take a bus to McNary. I did that for eight years. *That* was a lotta fun. In the morning y'get off the bus at the school, an' before you can get inside the door the white kids on the sidewalk're callin' you a dirty redskin. I wanted t'quit but the missionaries tol' my ma I was smarter'n most, an' she made me go anyway. By the time I got through high school, she had scraped up enough money for one semester's tuition at A&M, and here I am. Now I gotta make it on my own."

"It sounds like your mother cares a lot about you," I said, trying to keep him talking, but at the same time becoming intrigued by his story.

"She didn't have time to care for me *at all*. Sixty hours a week, she slings hash at a greasy spoon in Fort Apache, comes home, feeds the younger kids, and then tries to sober up my old man."

"Your father work?"

Longhorse barked a short laugh. "Only thing *he* works at is gettin' *drunk*. Almost every guy on the reservation—an' some of the women too— are drunks. If Geronimo could come back and see what's happened to his *warrior* ancestors, he'd scalp the whole lot of us." He jerked a thumb at his chest. "Lookit me—I'm gettin' just like th'rest of 'em."

"Oh? You get drunk every night?"

"Nah... not yet, at least. Tonight I was eating supper over at the NCO club, watchin' all them old sergeants—the ones who got houses and families here on base—wish the bartender a Merry Christmas and head home to wrap presents for the kids. I couldn't remember the last time I got a Christmas present, and first thing I knew I'd put away six or seven beers."

The missile temperatures were drifting up, so we went out to the FAT unit and tweaked the louvers. On the way back to the van, the chilly desert wind whipped harshly at us.

"Gawdamn, I hate cold," Longhorse complained, zipping up his wind-breaker.

"This isn't so cold."

"Mebbe not now," he said. "But come January, it'll get down to 'bout twenty degrees."

"*Twenty degrees*? Where I come from, twenty *below* is more like it in the winter."

"Twenty below *zero*? Yer fulla crap," Longhorse declared, flatly dismissing my comment. "Lissen, lemme tell you—we got no heat in the shack on the reservation. I used to lay on my mattress winter mornings watching my breath drift up to the ceiling."

I wasn't impressed. "We didn't have an inside toilet either. By five o'clock in the morning, when the fire in the wood stove had died, the piss in my chamber pot was frozen solid."

Longhorse drilled me with a fierce Apache scowl. "It's nice that you white men can afford chamber pots. In the middle of the night me and my brothers have to go outside in the desert. The women got it easier. They use tin cans." Inspired by his brilliant rebuttal, he continued. "An' the summers are worse'n that. The flies get so bad they sit on the table and fight us for what little food there is."

"I've seen your puny little desert flies," I scoffed. A Michigan mosquito would polish off a dozen of them for breakfast."

"We had no toys at'all," Longhorse said. "We used t'make bows and arrows outta tree branches."

"I was ten years old before I found out that you could buy new nails in a hardware store," I countered. "I always had to pull nails out of old vegetable crates to build toys with."

The gauntlet had been thrown. Using poverty for ammunition, we launched into verbal combat. Being a reservation Indian gave Longhorse an edge, but I wasn't about to concede. I had plenty of hardship stories of my own.

The time flew by as we went back and forth. Admittedly, I stretched the truth a time or two, but he probably did the same. The important thing was that the mental gymnastics were sobering him up.

By six a.m. I had to leave. The day shift would be arriving soon, and I wasn't supposed to be here.

"Hey, Chief Throwing Bull," I said sarcastically. "The missile temps are edging up. I know your thin Apache blood'll freeze up in this forty-degree weather, but since you're still on shift, why don't you zip up your jacket one more time and go out to adjust the fan vents?"

Longhorse playfully numbed my arm with a left jab and headed out to the FAT unit to make the adjustment. I stayed in the van and performed one last chore before taking off.

During the night I'd noticed that each time Longhorse made entries into the log book he had to ask me what time it was, so I hurriedly wrapped a small package in slightly used red and green gift paper and left it on the van table. At least he'd get *one* Christmas present this year. Anyway, a little material wealth might stop his preaching about how poor he was.

Driving the pickup back to the base, I should have been dog-tired after staying up all night but I was feeling good. The loneliness and self-pity had vanished. Dawn was still an hour off, and as I drove east I gazed through the upper windshield to see if there really *was* a bright star up there. I thought I saw one that stood out from the rest but couldn't be sure.

Friday, January 29th, 1954
Organ, New Mexico

The Gila Monster Bar and Grill was a ramshackle, wind-blown joint on US-70 in a tiny burg called Organ, halfway between White Sands and Las Cruces. I had passed it many times on my way to Las Cruces, but it had never occurred to me to purposely go there to eat. But today—my last day at White Sands—Bob Flint had invited me out for a farewell dinner, and for some reason the Gila Monster was his restaurant of choice.

We took seats at one of the scarred wooden tables. Flint must have been a regular, because a leathery-faced barmaid, without saying a word, brought two bottles of Miller High Life over to the table and didn't ask me for I.D. even though I was still three months shy of my twenty-first birthday. We ordered the house specialty—the thirty-five-cent chili and cheeseburger deluxe combo.

Flint took a long pull on his beer, draining half of the bottle. "This's good timing, y'know? You finishing the Viking jacket blueprint before leaving."

I nodded and took a tentative sip on my beer, glancing nervously around for any sign of the New Mexico State Police.

"We'll be taking delivery on the Viking thermal jacket in August," Flint added. "You *are* coming back in August, aren't you?"

"I'll be here... if I still have a job."

"Sure, but not the *same* job. How'd you like to be the project engineer on that Viking test next fall?"

He said it just as I was taking another sip, and about an ounce of beer went up my nose. "Project engineer? *Me*? I'll still be a couple years away from graduation."

I thought he was kidding. The lab had three project engineers—all senior people. They scheduled equipment, picked personnel, ironed out all the details, and generally ramrodded the whole test.

"Are you required to take management courses while you're an undergraduate?" Flint asked.

"Uh... I don't think so."

"Then it's about time you got some on-the-job training. You *do* want to be a manager some day, don't you?"

"I never gave it much thought."

That answer didn't satisfy Flint. "How do you think an engineer gets ahead? By telling *other* engineers what to do, that's how."

Just then the food came and we ate. Flint ordered another beer, but I left mine untouched, worrying that I might say something colossally stupid during what was turning into a pivotal moment in my career.

"Well, do you want the job?" Flint asked, spooning up the last of his chili.

"Sure—of course."

"You won't be sorry," he declared. "You want to get on the management track early. Be able to look at the overall scheme. And another thing—high salaries go hand in hand with high responsibilities.

"Take my word for it," Flint said as he squinted at the bill, did a quick mental calculation of the tip, and slipped a dime and three pennies under the edge of his dirty plate. "There's nothing wrong with being able to afford the better things in life."

The Molding of a Leader

**The University of Michigan
February - August 1954**

Tuesday, February 2nd, 1954
Owen House, Ann Arbor

From the street, it looked like a New Orleans bordello. Whoever owned Owen House—the university co-op where I elected to live this semester—obviously hadn't surrendered to good taste. It would have been an impressive, grand old Victorian landmark if it hadn't been painted pumpkin orange with bright blue window trim.

However, my skimpy budget didn't include elegant surroundings. Room and board at Owen House worked out to a dollar sixty-five a day, much cheaper than the rapidly rising dormitory fees.

I lugged my suitcases up the porch stairs and through the front door. The foyer, clinging to long-gone elegance with the original ornate wooden staircase, reeked of old carpeting, fried eggs, and burnt coal. No one was in sight as I took a quick survey of the ground floor.

The living room was furnished with Salvation Army rejects: a striped couch repaired with plaid patches, once-overstuffed chairs leaking white tufts onto the worn rug, and a chromed-legged kitchen table holding an old phonograph and stacks of records. There was no television set. This certainly wasn't the West Quad.

The dining room was crammed with long wooden tables and benches similar to the Enlisted Men's Mess at White Sands. I fervently hoped that the food would be better.

I picked up a mimeographed flyer from the stack on a table in the foyer:

CAN JOE McCARTHY'S WITCH
HUNTS DESTROY OUR AMERICAN
SOCIALIST AND COMMUNIST PARTIES?

Come to Lester House on Sunday 14 Feb at 2 o'clock to hear several co-op resident experts discuss this threat. Peanut butter sandwiches and coffee will be served.

If this wasn't a joke, it was unnerving. I'd have to be careful not to get mixed up with the wrong element here. I had my government secret clearance to think about.

A scrawny fellow wearing nothing but ragged, grayed underwear wandered into the foyer from the back of the house. He was unshaven and munching on a thick peanut butter sandwich.

"Who do I see about my room?" I asked.

He chewed for a long time, swallowed, but ignored the question. "You want furniss job," he said in a heavy European accent.

"What?"

"You haf to work four hours a week. Iss why it's cheap to liff here. Get furniss tending job. Iss good—yoost keep stoker full of coal. In couple months, weather warms up and you shut it down for rest of semester. Go to house meeting Sunday night. Iss when jobs are giffen out. You don't get good job, you get stuck with dishwashing or some other shitwurk."

I listened intently. I'd certainly had enough dishwashing at Red's Rite Spot to last me awhile, so I mentally filed away the information and thanked him.

I asked again about my room, and he led me into the cluttered kitchen and pointed to a door leading to the basement. It seems that's where the house manager lived. I made my way down dark stairs and knocked on a door across from large laundry sinks.

"Come in," a voice said through the closed door.

The small, narrow room was jammed with old, junky furniture. All sizes of water and sewer pipes ran across the ceiling. An iron-frame bunk bed was filled with people. One guy in the top bunk was reading a textbook, and another in the bottom bunk was necking with a buxom blonde.

"Excuse me. I'm looking for the house manager," I said, turning to leave. I had obviously gotten the wrong room.

The guy in the bottom bunk disengaged himself from the blonde. "I'm the house manager."

This guy was just another college kid. I had expected someone ancient like our West-Quad housemother.

He waited for me to state my business, not bothering to get out of the bunk. I introduced myself, explaining that I'd just arrived.

"Go up to the third floor," he said. "Turn right and go to the left front corner room. You're in there with two others."

"Welcome to Owen House," the blonde said from the shadows of the lower bunk.

"She doesn't live here," the house manager quickly explained. "She's a friend of mine."

I nodded and left. This *definitely* wasn't the West Quad.

Sunday, February 7th, 1954
Owen House

Judging from the varied accents, clothing styles, and skin color, the guys crowded into the Owen House living room must have come from all over the world. The air was blue with tobacco smoke as everyone puffed on cigarettes or pipes while we waited for the house meeting to begin.

Finally, the basement-dwelling house manager banged on an aluminum pot with a large spoon to call the meeting to order. His first order of business was to acquaint newcomers with the democratic student-owned, student-operated concept of university co-ops.

The meeting dragged on endlessly with questions and arguments as I waited impatiently for the good stuff—the job assignments. We finally got around to it.

Some jobs were popular, and some jobs no one wanted. Many, for example, wanted to be cooks, and great care had to be exercised to select only the experienced ones. House steward—the person who ordered the food—was another popular job and a vote had to be taken.

For some reason, *no one* wanted to be the house manager. The position was filled only after one of the older guys was coerced into it.

Finally, the job I'd been waiting for came up.

"Who wants to be the furnace tender?" the lame-duck house manager asked.

I immediately shot my hand into the air, dreading to see how many others would also respond.

My hand was the only one raised. I couldn't believe my good luck.

The house manager nodded at me and made a note on his clipboard. "You got it. See Boris Kozlovich for details."

"Who's he?" I asked.

"The current furnace tender—the one giving up the job." The house manager pointed to someone behind me.

I turned around. It was the guy I'd met last Tuesday—the one who urged me to volunteer for the furnace-tending job.

As soon as the meeting was over, I collared Kozlovich and we went down in the basement to see the furnace. Half the furnace room was filled with a large pile of coal that had been poured in through the basement window. The other half was taken up with the huge furnace and the connecting stoker.

The stoker was a big metal box that held coal. A worm gear in a connecting metal tube that ran along the floor fed the coal from the stoker to the furnace. According to Kozlovich, all I had to do was shovel coal into the stoker.

"Iss ull automatic," Kozlovich explained, pointing at the stoker. "You feed coal to stoker, stoker feeds coal to furniss. Iss simple."

"How come you didn't want to keep on tending the furnace?" I asked Kozlovich, amazed that he would surrender such a soft job.

Kozlovich just shrugged.

Thursday, February 11th, 1954
Owen House

The cook hit the dinner buzzer, and the entire population of Owen House stampeded into the dining room. Pork chops were being served tonight—a great delicacy on a penny-pinching budget where macaroni and cheese was king.

My mother had always harped on one thing: if I didn't get anything else out of college, at least I'd become a gentleman. For example, learning proper table manners would enable me to dine with high-toned people and ultimately become a successful person who she could be proud of.

I wasn't making much progress in this area. Eating at Owen House had systematically eroded whatever primitive table manners I'd brought with me.

The meals were served family style with everyone helping himself. First helpings had to be modest or you were branded a pig, but second helpings—*if* there was anything left—were allowed after you cleaned your plate. Naturally, everyone ate as fast as possible so they could get seconds. It was the law of the jungle—fast eaters flourished and put on weight, while the slow ones either wasted away or eventually moved out to seek a less-hostile environment.

Tonight, I sat across from Walt Kilmer, an accomplished co-op chowhound with several years of competitive eating under his belt. Next to him sat Chiao-Min Chung, a plump South Korean who had just arrived from Seoul.

A large platter of sizzling pork chops was placed on the table and everyone dove in. Chung committed the cardinal sin of taking three pork chops the first time around, instead of the allowable two. He was a newcomer to our country so no one said anything, but it was duly noted.

No one talked. The only sound in the dining room was teeth tearing into flesh.

Kilmer finally broke the silence. "Look," he cried, pointing at the window. "Flamingos!"

Chiao-Min Chung, unfamiliar with North American wildlife, looked out the window, momentarily taking his eyes off his dinner plate. With cobra-like speed, Kilmer speared a pork chop from Chung's plate and had it three-quarters eaten by the time Chung looked back.

"They flew away," Kilmer explained when Chung looked at him questioningly. Chung stared down at his plate, thinking he had taken more pork chops than what he saw, but in the melee at the platter he couldn't be sure.

Gnawing furiously through my first helping, I was hungrily eyeing the remaining pork chops on the platter when the room began filling with smoke.

"Furnace man!" someone cried.

Everyone chimed in. "Furnace man! Furnace man!"

I continued eating. Surely, someone else had to be in charge of putting out fires. I just shovelled coal into the stoker.

"Furnace man! Go fix the stoker!"

The stoker? How could the stoker cause all this smoke? Reluctantly, I left my plate and went down to the basement.

Thick smoke was billowing out from the furnace room. Coughing my way in, I discovered that it was indeed coming from the stoker. I jerked the lid open and saw the smoke drifting up through the unburned coal in the stoker. The smoke was coming from the furnace through the worm-gear duct.

The fire in the furnace was very low. The stoker wasn't pumping coal, but why not?.

I ran back up to the dining room and found Kozlovich.

"I need help," I cried.

"Rock in worm gear," he said.

"What?"

"Rock from coal pile gets in worm gear. Stops stoker. Iss why you get smoke. You take out rock, stoker runs, no more smoke. Iss simple." He took another bite from a pork chop.

"You never told me about rocks," I said accusingly. "Come show me."

The smoke was getting thicker, and the guys in the dining room were now yelling at both Kozlovich and me. With a resigned sigh, Kozlovich grabbed two pork chops and followed me to the basement.

Placing the pork chops on top of the stoker, Kozlovich knelt down and removed the cover from the worm gear assembly. The gear was packed with ground coal, but his fingers expertly probed the mechanism and extracted a rock.

"You haff to look out for rocks when you put coal in stoker." With coal-blackened fingers he took one of the pork chops off the stoker and resumed eating.

I stared at the rock Kozlovich had just removed from the worm gear box. It looked like just another lump of coal. This job was getting complicated.

"Do we restart the stoker now?" I asked.

"Not yet. Must put in new shear pin."

"Shear pin? What shear pin?"

"Worm gear can't grind up rock—too hard. Too much torque on gear shaft snaps shear pin." Kozlovich dipped his hand back into the gear assembly and pulled out a tiny piece of metal. He held it in his hand for my inspection.

"It looks like a piece of a nail," I said.

"Iss right. Stoker made in Zinzinnati. Too expensiff to get shear pins from Zinzinnati. We make out uff nails. Come, I show you."

Kozlovich led me into the basement workshop where he carefully selected a certain-size nail and cut off the tip with a hacksaw. Back in the furnace room, he inserted this homemade shear pin into the worm gear shaft and pressed a restart button— which I hadn't even noticed—on the bottom of the stoker. The stoker started right up. In a matter of minutes, the smoke was clearing.

"How often does this happen?" I asked, feverishly trying to memorize everything Kozlovich had done.

"Nut often. Mebbe two, three times a week."

"Is there anything else I gotta know about this job?" I asked sarcastically.

"No," Kozlovich replied cheerfully, "Iss simple job. I go now. Haf to wash dinner dishes."

"Wait a minute—wait a minute—you gave up this job to *wash dishes*?"

Kozlovich shrugged and left the furnace room chomping on his last pork chop.

Saturday, February 20th, 1954
Owen House

The furnace-tending job and on-going battle for food weren't my only problems at Owen House.

Co-op rookies were put into the worst accommodations in the house— the third floor. Nine of us slept in a large army-barracks-style bunk room. It paid to be dog-tired when you went to bed, because the combined snoring rattled the windows.

The rest of the floor was divided up into three-man study rooms. These rooms—crammed under the eaves of the house—were small, with sloping walls running from the baseboard to the house ridgepole. The only place in the room where you could stand up straight was in the very middle. It was like studying in a pup tent with two other people.

In true co-op fashion, racial and ethnic equality was observed at all times. I was in a study room with Abdul Baki and Saul Rosensweig, an Arab and a Jew. At first, I thought nothing of it, thanks to my abysmal ignorance of Middle East politics. That quickly changed.

With Baki and Rosensweig, it was mutual hatred at first sight. Baki, whose father was a wealthy merchant in Beirut, Lebanon, would never have willingly associated with an infidel like Rosensweig. Rosensweig, a swarthy, brooding Brooklynite, often spoke with pride of relatives battling militant Arab hordes in order to exist on a kibbutz near Jerusalem.

The semester had just begun when Baki and Rosensweig got into a scuffle in the third-floor bathroom. Rosensweig fell on the tile floor and injured his leg. As soon as he was able, he consulted with attorneys in downtown Ann Arbor to press for a lawsuit against Baki. None would take the case.

After the bathroom incident, Baki began opening his mail with a large curved-blade dagger, leaving it conspicuously on his desk within easy reach. Not to be outdone, Rosensweig began cleaning his fingernails with a top-of-the-line Swiss army knife containing a thousand various sharp instruments, each capable of inflicting serious injury. I had my trusty slide rule for protection.

All of these inconveniences and problems would have been bearable if I'd had a social life. Ruth and I had kept up a steady, if not passionate, correspondence while I was at White Sands, but unfortunately I'd seen very little of her since the semester began. She was devoted to her parents and was now living with them in Detroit, commuting to Ann Arbor three times a week for classes. This schedule was stifling any hope of romance. We had managed only a few brief daytime coffee dates since the semester began.

But tonight all of that was about to change. Ruth had invited me to Saturday-night dinner at her parents' home. I was going to meet Mr. and Mrs. J. B. Grimsby, an encouraging sign knowing how Ruth felt about them.

It would be a long bus ride to Detroit, so at three in the afternoon I had already taken over the third-floor bathroom, attempting to make myself presentable.

I stared at my haggard face in the mirror as I shaved. Had Owen House aged me that much in only *two weeks*? Upon closer inspection I saw the reason. Coal dust. Microscopic wrinkles—normally invisible on my twenty-year-old face—had become imbedded with coal dust from filling the stoker five times a day. I was starting to look like my old man!

I hurried down to my room and got the heavy-duty Lava soap I used for cleaning my hands after shovelling coal. Working up a gritty lather, I scoured my face till it was raw. It did no good.

As I finished shaving, I tried to think of an explanation to give the Grimsby's. Perhaps I could tell them I was an old World War II veteran, even making some oblique references to action in the Pacific.

"Furnace man! Furnace man!" Somebody downstairs was yelling.

I stepped out onto the third-floor landing and sniffed the air, my nose now highly trained in detecting stoker smoke. The air was clear—probably a false alarm just to get my goat. I went back into the bathroom.

"Furnace man! We got no hot water!"

Hot water? Now I *knew* someone was pulling my leg—trying to rattle me because I had a hot date in Detroit. I ignored the shout, stripped down, and turned on the shower.

There was no hot water.

The new house manager came into the bathroom. "The pilot light on the water heater's gone out. You've got to relight it."

"Me? Why me?"

"The water heater's in the furnace room—haven't you noticed it? Everything in there is your responsibility. Didn't Kozlovich explain that?"

I knew nothing about water heaters. In fact, we didn't even *have* a water heater in Upper Michigan. My mother heated water in a copper boiler on our wood stove. My grandmother was the only one in the whole clan who had a water heater, and any relative who couldn't stand saunas—like me— trooped over to her house on Saturday night to take a shower.

I got dressed and stopped by Kozlovich's room on the second floor.

"I don't know vatter heaters," he said. "It neffer vent out last semester."

Kozlovich's roommate—Hiroshi Kunimoto from Japan—got caught up in the discussion and volunteered to help. Kunimoto didn't have any experience with water heaters either, but he had seen the one in his father's bath house in Yokohama and felt qualified to assist.

The three of us went down to the furnace room. After looking the water heater over, we removed a small metal cover plate on the bottom. Instructions for lighting the pilot light were printed on the inside of the plate.

The bottom compartment of the heater housed the pilot light, the gas burner, and the temperature controls, but it was difficult to see anything in the bad light. We didn't have a flashlight, so we took a long strip of cardboard from a coat hanger, set one end ablaze and stuck it in the opening to shed some light.

"There's the pilot-light tube," Kunimoto observed as we peered in. "The instructions say to heat that tube up for a minute with a flame, press the red button, and light the pilot. Sounds simple."

We proceeded to do that. It didn't work. Relighting the cardboard, we stuck it under the pilot-light tube again. Nothing.

"Not doing it right," Kozlovich exclaimed. "Must press button down while heating tube."

"The instructions don't say that," I replied.

"Vaat do instructions know? Ziss ting probably made in Zinzinnati like zat crappy stoker. Ve try it."

We heated up the tube again, this time keeping the red button pressed down all the while. The cardboard torch went out. As I was relighting it with Kozlovich's cigarette lighter, we heard a hissing sound.

"Zee? I vas right," Kozlovich exclaimed, keeping his finger on the button. "You can hear gas coming into pilot-light tube."

"Are you sure it's just gas to the *pilot light*?" Kunimoto wondered. "It sounds loud."

By now the three of us were on our hands and knees on the floor, butts up in the air, all looking into the bottom compartment of the water heater. I stuck the flaming cardboard torch in to light the pilot light.

KKKAAAA———-WWWHHUUUMMMPPP!!!!!!!!!!!

The blast bowled us over. Terror-stricken, we jumped up and rushed for the door.

Three of us—shoulder to shoulder to shoulder—were too wide for the furnace-room door. We bounced off the door jamb and fell back on the floor.

We checked ourselves over. Everyone seemed to be okay, except I kept seeing a white blob of light that refused to go away. My face felt very hot.

"I tink I know how to light it now," Kozlovich said thoughtfully.

"Your eyebrows are gone," I told him.

"Go look in mirror," Kozlovich replied. "Yours gone too."

To reach the quiet, tree-lined street where Ruth's parents lived, I had to transfer twice on the Detroit metropolitan bus system. I pressed the door-bell on the dark imposing brownstone. A soft chime sounded somewhere deep within the house.

I was nervous. After the water heater explosion I had cleaned up the best I could, but even with my good clothes on I still looked like hell.

Ruth opened the door, smiled, then grew concerned when she got a good look at me.

"What happened? Your face is all red, and—ohmigosh—your eyebrows are gone!"

"There was this explosion..."

"Explosion?" a man's voice behind Ruth interjected. A distinguished-looking gentleman—obviously Mr. Grimsby—appeared, gently nudging his daughter aside to get a better look at me.

Ruth had told me that her father was the superintendent of a high school in Detroit, and his appearance indeed reflected a position of some influence. He wore a brown tweed suit, complete with vest. A heavy chain disappearing into his watch pocket was weighted down with assorted gold Greek letters, denoting membership to various honorary academic societies. His jowls were pink from a close shave but, of course, not nearly as pink as mine.

"Are you all right, son?" he asked, staring at my face where my eye-brows should have been.

"Oh, yessir. We were just trying to relight a water heater and got too much gas around the pilot light. Everybody's okay—even the water heater." I chuckled lightheartedly, implying that I encountered problems like that every day and it was no big deal.

I was led into a wood-panelled dining room, lit only by tall candles on a snowy white tablecloth. I twitched, the candles reminding me of the card-board torch I had been jabbing into the water heater just hours before.

*"Are you all right, son?" he asked, staring at my face
where my eyebrows should have been.*

Mrs. Grimsby came in from the kitchen. She forced a gracious smile as we were being introduced, no doubt wondering all the while how her daughter could possibly have become involved with such a grotesque-looking person.

Over our salads, Mr. Grimsby began the fatherly duty of interrogating his daughter's suitor.

"Water heater, you say? Don't you live in a men's dormitory? They must have maintenance people to take care of that sort of thing."

"I no longer live in a dormitory, sir. I'm now in a co-op house. The students run the house—the whole operation. I'm in charge of the furnace and the water heater. Kozlovich, Kunimoto, and I were trying to relight the pilot light when the explosion occurred."

"Kozlovich?—Kunimoto?—these people are foreigners?"

"Yessir. Kunimoto is from Japan. I don't know exactly where Kozlovich is from... Europe someplace, I guess."

Grimsby scowled. "Sounds *Russian* to me."

"Could be, sir. Co-op houses attract a lot of foreign students. It's because we practice democratic principles—one member, one vote. We have open membership regardless of race, politics, or religion." During my short time at Owen House, I had become fluent in the co-op argot.

Grimsby put down his salad fork and stared at me like an irate father. "Do you know who Senator Joseph McCarthy is?" he asked quietly.

I nodded, getting the distinct feeling I wasn't making a good impression on Grimsby.

"Senator McCarthy is trying to make the country aware that the Communist menace is everywhere—industry, the military, even universities! Don't you realize that anyplace that advertises open membership, regardless of race, politics, or religion, is a breeding ground for communism?"

The conversation was getting much too intense for Mrs. Grimsby, and she hurried out to the kitchen to attend to the main course. I looked over at Ruth, hoping for some support, but she was staring down at her salad plate.

Things settled down once Mrs. Grimsby returned with a platter of lamb chops and vegetable side dishes. I took two chops—the standard allotment for the first helping—a big scoop of mashed potatoes, and string beans. I dug in. Eating was more up my alley than discussing Joe McCarthy.

Grimsby opened a new subject. "You're majoring in engineering, is that right?"

"Yessir," I said, a large mouthful of lamb chop muffling my reply.

Grimsby relaxed a bit, relieved to discuss an academic subject, even if it *was* engineering. "What kind of engineering? Mechanical? Civil? Chemical?"

I swallowed quickly. "I haven't really started to take specialized courses, sir, but I do know one thing—I want to work with rockets."

Mrs. Grimsby was pouring gravy onto Ruth's mashed potatoes and almost dropped the ladle on the tablecloth. "Rockets?" she shrilled, obviously thinking of Fourth of July fireworks.

Grimsby screwed up his mouth as if he had bitten into something rotten. "Rockets? What kind of rockets?"

"Large ones, sir," I exclaimed enthusiastically. "Rockets that will take instruments into outer space. Someday we'll be sending a satellite into orbit around the earth."

"A satellite? Ridiculous! That'll cost a million dollars! Who would pay for it?"

"Well... I don't know, sir. I hadn't really given it much thought."

"That's the trouble with this world. No one ever thinks about who's going to pay the bills. Perhaps you'd better consider specializing in building schools or bridges—something that will benefit society. Besides, those rockets can be dangerous, I would think."

"Yessir! They explode all the time down at White Sands!"

I immediately wished I hadn't said that. To make matters even worse, I had unconsciously launched into my top-speed eating mode that I'd used to such good advantage in the Owen House dining room. I had loaded two more lamb chops onto my plate and had them about chowed down when I noticed that the three of them—just getting started on their first helping—were staring at me.

Friday, March 19th, 1954
A Lester House Hootenany, Ann Arbor

There once was a Union maid,
Who never was afraid,
Of goons and ginks and company finks
And deputy sheriffs who made the raids;

*L*ed by two acoustic guitars, the crowd in the living room of Lester House—a women's co-op—were singing old union songs and various other protest dittys. I knew all the currently popular tunes but not these on the co-op'ers hit parade. "Union Maid" was the final song in a medley urging the downtrodden workers to rise up against the cruelty and indifference of greedy capitalist bosses. If Joe McCarthy had been at Lester House tonight, he would have been taking down names.

But I wasn't concerned about McCarthy, blacklists, or anything else so mundane. I was looking for women.

It was over between Ruth and me. She obviously put a lot of stock in her father's opinions because last month's disastrous dinner had torpedoed our struggling romance. I called her several times afterward but couldn't even get a coffee date.

So, after six hectic weeks of dealing with differential equations, thermodynamic heat engines, a malicious coal stoker, and two roommates whose fervent wish was to kill one another, I was on the prowl for female companionship. She could even be a communist for all I cared.

There was a break in the singing as refreshments were served— canned sardines on toothpicks, peanut butter and Ritz cracker sandwiches, and some kind of cheap wine that came in gallon jugs.

I surveyed the women, knowing that the five dollars in my pocket would enable me to treat any one of them to a far more lavish experience than a co-op hootenany.

I bent over a woman sitting crosslegged on the carpet. "Hi, my name is Jerry..."

She produced an unlit cigarette out of nowhere and held it in her fingers. "Got a light?"

I dug out a wooden kitchen match, the accepted co-op cigarette lighter. I looked around for someplace to strike it. Nothing.

She snatched the match from my hand and scratched the match head with her thumbnail, setting it ablaze. "Thanks," she said dryly, turning away to resume her conversation with one of the guitar players.

That's okay, I thought—there are plenty of other fish in the sea. In fact, two fairly attractive fish were talking near the refreshment table, which now held a large, metal mixing bowl filled with punch.

Employing my most engaging smile I said, "Hi, can I get you two a cup of punch?" The two women looked at me for a moment, then nodded.

I quickly filled three paper cups with the yellowish punch and handed them each one. I took a gulp of mine.

My throat was immediately paralyzed. "What *is* this?" I wheezed. My eyes began to water.

One of the woman took a sip. "Oh, it's that stuff the guys over in Nakamura House mix up," she remarked offhandedly. "Grapefruit juice and grain alcohol. Somebody should get after them. It's a bit strong."

The other one tossed her punch off with one gulp, turned to me, and said, "Maybe you can settle the argument we're having. Where was Joe Hill executed: Utah or Colorado?"

"Joe Hill?" I croaked.

"You know... the famous Wobbly organizer."

"Wobbly?" *I* was feeling a little wobbly.

"Wobbly—the IWW—the Industrial Workers of the World. You're new to co-ops, aren't you?" she stated. The guitars started up again and the two left me to join the singers.

It was clear that I hadn't absorbed enough co-op culture to socialize effectively, so I decided to leave and drown my sorrows with skim milk and a peanut butter sandwich at Owen House.

As I proceeded to the front door, head down, I ran smack into a woman—a full-body collision with all four of our arms locking up.

At first glance she appeared to be older than the rest—perhaps the Lester housemother—but looking more closely as we disengaged, I realized it wasn't age wrinkles on her forehead. *It was coal dust!*

She also looked at *my* face with interest. "You're a furnace tender," she said softly.

"Over at Owen House. You are too, aren't you?"

"Right here at Lester."

"The weather's finally warming up." I knew that she would fully appreciate the significance of the remark.

She smiled, the spider webs of coal dust cracking around her mouth. "Isn't it wonderful? I only have to fill the stoker three times a day now."

"Been having much trouble with rocks in the coal?" My dialogue now seemed to flow effortlessly.

"Oh, yes." Her laughter tinkled like a fairy's bell. "But I'm almost out of shear pins."

"Almost out? I make my own."

Her breathing became rapid. She looked into my eyes and licked her lips. "You *make* your own shear pins?"

"Why don't I take you over to my workshop in the basement. I'll show you my shear pins."

We filled up two paper cups with cheap wine and went out into the crisp evening.

Friday, April 16th, 1954
The Pretzel Bell
Downtown Ann Arbor

It was a time-honored tradition at the University of Michigan to make a pilgrimage to the Pretzel Bell—a downtown Ann Arbor beer hall commonly known as the P-Bell—to have your first legal drink. Letch Sternitzky and Boris Kozlovich were going down there with me tonight to celebrate my twenty-first birthday.

At first, Kozlovich didn't want to go. "I haf no money for beer," he complained. "Iss serious. Still owe co-op for room and board dis semester."

"When someone turns twenty-one, the P-Bell springs for a free pitcher of beer," I explained. "It won't cost you a cent."

When we arrived at the P-Bell, our I.D.'s were checked at the door.

"We got one!" the checker yelled, noting that I had turned twenty-one that day. One of the waiters exuberantly rang a large bell hung prominently over the middle of the bar, broadcasting to the whole world that I was now *legal.* Brazen hoots and shrill whistles erupted from the boisterous crowd.

Like VIP's, we were ceremoniously ushered to an empty table. Three glasses and a frosty pitcher of beer were placed before us.

The hard-eyed crowd turned to me and began an ominous chant.

"CHUG-A-LUG, CHUG-A-LUG, CHUG-A-LUG..."

Chug-a-lugging—drinking an entire glass of beer without stopping—was a popular college sport in those days, and the P-Bell was the chug-a-lug capital of Ann Arbor. All brand-new twenty-one-year-olds were obligated to chug-a-lug the first glass from the P-Bell's free pitcher of beer. It didn't sound like much until you saw the size of the glass.

A waiter obligingly filled the huge beer glass and handed it to me.

The crowd kept thundering, "CHUG-A-LUG, CHUG-A-LUG, CHUG-A -LUG..."

I took a deep, nervous breath, shut my eyes, hoisted the heavy glass, and began to drink. Eighty-five swallows later and still drinking, I opened my eyes, praying that all I would be looking at was the empty bottom of the glass. All I could see was beer.

The beer began backing up into passages not designed for holding beer. With a humongous choking sneeze, I exploded, spraying beer out of every hole in my head.

No one was sympathetic. The surly crowd of upperclassmen booed and hissed at my failure to empty the glass. They resumed their drinking, waiting for another newly minted twenty-one-year-old to appear at the door.

Totally embarrassed, I mopped the beer off my face with a handkerchief, hoping to finish off the free pitcher and slink out before the mob came up with another bizarre ritual to perform.

As the three of us drank, Kozlovich was critical of the draft beer. "Iss very veak—like vater. Beer in Euroop much better."

The most vocal of my chug-a-lug critics had been six big bozos overflowing the wooden chairs at an adjoining table. They looked like a jock fraternity out on the town, all decked out in matching dark blue blazers, neatly pressed gray slacks, and pink dress shirts with tight-fitting narrow collars around necks that were larger than my chest.

Their table was littered with empty beer pitchers, attesting to some serious guzzling. The biggest guy—a three-hundred pounder, I guessed—was giving a clinic on major-league chug-a-lugging. A stopwatch was being used to measure his time. With three colossal swallows he could drain a twenty-ounce glass in less than two seconds.

When one of his cronies challenged him to a chug-a-lugging contest, we could hear the rules being set down. No more than one inch of foam allowed in the glass; spillage of beer spelled automatic disqualification; each man was to start with his right forearm flat on the table, hand around the glass; and at the signal, chug-a-lugging would begin. The first to place his empty glass down on the table would win.

Two glasses were filled. The huge adversaries clutched the beer glasses in their mammoth mitts, glaring at each other as they waited for the signal.

"CHUG!" cried an appointed referee at their table.

Both beer glasses shot up to open mouths, both heads jerked back, and both Adam's apples bobbed furiously as the beer instantly disappeared.

"BAM!—BAM!" The bottoms of the two empty beer glasses smacked the heavily scarred wooden table in rapid succession.

The challenger was good but not good enough. Wheezing and gasping for air, he slowly shook his head, acknowledging defeat.

"Gawd, that's amazing," I commented.

"Too much swallow," Kozlovich observed.

"Whaddaya mean?"

"Too much swallow slows drinking."

"Slows drinking? Wadda *you* know about chug-a-lugging, Kozlovich? That guy's probably the fastest beer drinker in the world!"

The beaten challenger extended his hand across the table toward the champ in a gesture of good sportsmanship. But as they shook hands, a twenty-dollar bill covertly changed ownership.

"Did you see that?" I whispered to Kozlovich.

Kozlovich nodded dumbly. Twenty dollars represented two weeks room and board at Owen House.

Kozlovich dug into his pocket and brought out a handful of money. He counted the dollar bills and silver.

"I haf four dollars fifty-fife cents. How much you two haf?"

"Why do you wanna know?" Sternitzky asked suspiciously.

"I need fifteen dollars forty-fife cents," Kozlovich stated.

I knew what he was up to. "Kozlovich, if you're thinking about taking on that moose in a chug-a-lugging contest, you're crazy. He'll kill you."

"You're not getting any of my money," Sternitzky declared.

"Iss a loan only. No matter vat heppens, Monday morning I pay back everyting... plus ten percent."

"Kozlovich, I thought you were broke," I said.

"I haf little money in benk—not much."

Sternitzky's eyes narrowed. "Ten percent interest, win or lose? How do I know you'll do it?"

"You haf my vord on it."

We counted out our money. I had six dollars and twenty-eight cents, and Sternitzky came up with the rest. "I'll need that back to pay lab fees next week," he warned.

Kozlovich scooped up the cash, stuffed it in his shirt pocket, and approached the chug-a-lug champ.

"I vish to drink beer vit you... to, how you say... chug the lug."

The jocks were highly amused by Kozlovich's quaint speech and shabby appearance.

"I thought Bohemians only drank wine," one of them cracked.

"Put 'im under the table, Goliath," another advised the chug-a-lugging champ. "One glass ought'a do it."

Goliath took in Kozlovich's wrinkled clothes and unshaven jowls. "This is a private party," he sneered, turning back to his friends.

Kozlovich said, "Mebbe you like small vager on beer drinking."

"You don't have enough money."

"Tvanty dollars enuff?"

Goliath's eyes flickered. "You got twenty dollars?" He thought for a second. "Nah. I'd like to take your money, but..."

Kozlovich nodded as if in agreement. "Perheps iss batter dis vay. You slow drinker—mebbe need more practiss."

Goliath's buddies howled with delight at that. The audacity of this bummy-looking character standing up to their leader was hilarious.

Goliath slowly lumbered to his feet and towered over Kozlovich. "Show me your money," he rasped under his beery breath. "Don't flash it—the management frowns on gambling. I just wanna make sure this is gonna be worth my while."

Kozlovich exposed the shirt-pocket roll of bills—most of them ones—enough to give Goliath a look.

A chair next to Goliath was provided for Kozlovich, and the contest rules were repeated. Kozlovich filled up his glass from my free pitcher, and the two of them squared off.

"CHUG!"

The glasses of beer flew to their mouths, then BAM!... BAM!—the empties hit the table.

It wasn't as close as Goliath's previous match, no surprise there. The surprise was that Kozlovich was the victor.

Goliath had his head tilted back, so he didn't see how Kozlovich had managed it. All he knew was that when he slammed his glass down, Kozlovich already had his on the table.

It was really quite simple—at least in theory. Kozlovich didn't swallow. He just tilted his head back and poured the beer down his throat. My gawd, I thought, you couldn't dump it on the floor any faster.

It was *so* fast, in fact, that Goliath's friends thought it was a magic trick and peered under the table around Kozlovich's chair, looking for the missing beer.

Goliath grudgingly palmed a twenty over to Kozlovich. Certain that he had been the victim of bad luck, he grumbled to Kozlovich, "Again?"

Kozlovich let loose a tremendous belch and nodded.

Again the glasses were filled, and again Kozlovich won.

"Take 'im on again, Goliath," a crony growled. "He may be fast, but he's small. He'll get crocked."

That made sense to Goliath. "Another?" he muttered to Kozlovich.

Kozlovich, now forty dollars richer, studiously adjusted the steel-rimmed spectacles on his nose as he pretended to give the matter some serious thought. "Vhy not?"

Three rounds later Kozlovich was still undefeated. The pace had quickened so much that Goliath had stopped palming twenties across the table and had begun running a tab. I was busily calculating Kozlovich's winnings on a napkin.

But by now the beer was having an effect on Kozlovich. He was having trouble focussing his eyes and had totally abandoned his marginal English, lapsing into his native Russian which, of course, no one understood.

Goliath, though red-faced and glassy-eyed himself, picked up on this. Realizing that his weight advantage was finally having an effect, he decided to go for the kill.

"One last beer. Double or nothing on what I owe."

Sensing that chug-a-lugging history was in the making, P-Bell customers began leaving their tables to gather around Goliath and Kozlovich. A waiter silently brought a fresh pitcher of beer to the table.

Kozlovich had already won a hundred dollars and could lose it all; but he nodded and the glasses were filled once more. The crowd tensed with anticipation. Sternitzky, knowing intuitively that anyone with such highly specialized skills needed attending to, jumped up and began massaging the sides of Kozlovich's neck so the beer would find a relaxed passageway.

"CHUG!"

Goliath, although slower than before, was still putting the beer away at a pretty good clip. But Kozlovich was in trouble. Whereas the beer had been gushing down his throat in a torrent, it was now just a trickle.

Kozlovich still had most of his beer left when Goliath, with his head back, drained the last drop from his upended glass. Eyes closed and lips still on the rim of the empty glass, he remained thus poised, obviously savoring the sweet taste of victory.

"Put the glass on the table!" one of his cronies cried.

Goliath didn't do that. Instead, he began to lean further back very slowly, his chair tilting at a precarious angle.

"Timber!" Sternitzky yelled.

With a thunderous crash, Goliath fell over backwards, chair and all, on the floor. He was out cold. One of his buddies tried to pry the empty beer glass from his huge hand to put it on the table, hoping to somehow win the match, but Goliath had a death grip on it.

Finally, Kozlovich banged his empty glass down on the tabletop, triumphantly shouting a Russian word with a lot of k's, y's, and z's in it.

The P-Bell took an exceedingly dim view of people being rendered unconscious by their beer, and two waiters rushed over with sopping wet bar rags which they wrung out over Goliath's face.

Sternitzky—Kozlovich's self-appointed manager—leaned over Goliath on the floor. "You lost. Pay up!"

"Not nuff money," Goliath mumbled. "How 'boutta check?"

*With a thunderous crash, Goliath fell over backwards,
chair and all, on the floor. He was out cold.*

"Cash only—no checks!" Sternitzky hissed.

Goliath's cronies, sobered by defeat, quickly took up a collection and slipped the cash to Sternitzky who promptly took out his ten-dollar lab-fee money, plus ten percent, of course. We got up and left the P-Bell.

The fresh air revived Kozlovich, and he reflected on his new-found wealth as we walked down Packard Street toward home.

"I tink I go to summer school dis year. Joost for fun. Mebbe take Engliss literature courses or someding like dat." He started walking faster. "But right now I must get to houss. Use toilet."

"How'd you learn to drink like that?," Sternitzky asked, thinking there might be a lucrative career in chug-a-lugging.

"Iss simple," Kozlovich answered, breaking into a trot as we neared the co-op house. "Ve used to haf... how you say it... contests... like dat in Roossia." Then he added, "but with wodka, not dis vatery beer."

Friday, June 11th, 1954
The Blue Front News Stand, Ann Arbor

I had to call home. The news was too exciting to just put in a letter. Besides, a letter could take five or six days to get to Upper Michigan.

Long-distance phone calls couldn't be made from the telephone at Owen House, so I trotted down to the pay phone in the Blue Front News Stand on Packard Street. I hurriedly stuffed in quarters, dimes, and nickels. The operator, after counting the various clinks, connected me.

"Hello."

"Hi, Pop, it's me."

"Whut's wrong?"

I tried to sound calm. "Nothing's wrong. I just felt like calling instead of writing a letter."

"It only cost three cents t'mail a letter."

"I'm fixed okay. I still got money, and I'll be going back to work at White Sands in August."

"Whut's on yer mind?" the old man said, still attempting to keep the call short and cheap.

"Well, there's one thing. I just got elected house manager at Owen House for the summer session.

"Yer gonna run the place?"

"Yessir. I wanna get some practice managing because Mr. Flint, my boss down at White Sands, is going to make me a project engineer in August. He says that management is the way to go for engineers."

"Sometimes people don't always wanna do what they're supposed to," the old man advised.

I chuckled at the remark. "These are college men, Pop. They know their responsibilities and take them seriously."

"Even so, bein' a boss kin still be tricky."

I laughed again.

My mother got on the line. "How is your schoolwork going?"

"I'm all done with spring classes. I got one A and the rest B's."

"You did better than that in high school."

"This isn't high school," I said testily. "It's the best I've done down here."

"Well, maybe you can do better this summer if you don't chase around too much."

"I'll try, Ma."

Walking back to Owen House, my mind fairly brimmed over with innovative management ideas. Who knows—with a little planning, I might even be able to reduce the weekly work assignments from four hours to three. Everyone would like that.

Monday, June 14th, 1954
The Owen-House Kitchen

Mohatt Nandi, the eldest son of a wealthy Calcutta merchant, drew himself up to his full five-foot-seven-inch height. "At my father's home," he declared in his clipped British accent, "we *hire* people to do this type of work."

The sink was stacked high with dirty dishes, pots, and pans from dinner. This was my first day as house manager, and I was explaining to Nandi that it was his job to wash them.

"Everyone's got to put in four hours of work every week, Mohatt. You didn't volunteer for any of the other jobs at the house meeting, so you were assigned to dishwashing."

Nandi sniffed indignantly. "I wish to reconsider. Surely there must be something else available, perhaps a position dealing with people, similar to what you do as house manager."

"All those jobs've been taken. You've got to wash dishes, Mohatt."

"I would *never* have to do such a thing in Calcutta. I had heard that university cooperatives have a democratic environment. Equal rights and freedom of choice. Obviously, I was mistaken if I am being forced to perform menial labor such as this."

Frustrated, I groped for another approach.

Kozlovich, building an after-dinner peanut butter sandwich near the refrigerator, overheard the conversation. "Iss simple. Either vash dishes or move out."

Nandi glared at him as he snatched the apron from the wall hook and put it on.

I made a mental note. Ultimatums—a good management tool.

Wednesday, June 30th, 1954
The Office of the Dean of Women

Management was much more complicated than I first thought. Today for example, I was flattening my tailbone on a hard oak chair in the Dean of Women's outer office and didn't even know why I was there. It must have had something to do with being the Owen House manager though, because sitting next to me was Gloria Greeley, the manager from Stevens House, a women's co-op. Dean Deborah Barker had requested that both of us report to her office today at two p.m.

Whatever the reason, the meeting promised to be exciting because Gloria was an intense, wild-eyed law student with a reputation for sinking her fangs into social injustices, especially those levied by the university bureaucracy.

I nervously drummed my fingers on the arm of the chair, wishing for a cigarette, but there were no ashtrays around. That didn't slow Gloria down one bit; she lit up and was flicking the ashes into the cuff of her jeans.

Finally, the inner office door opened, and Dean Barker stuck her head out. "Come in please."

Gloria tamped the cigarette out on the heel of her boot and placed the long butt in her shirt pocket, saving it for a future smoke. We went in and stood in front of Dean Barker's desk. The dean briefly shuffled a few papers around, then opened the discussion.

"You two are the managers of the Owen and Stevens cooperative houses?"

"Yes, ma'am," I answered. Gloria just nodded.

"I'll get right to the point," Barker continued. "My office has received a complaint from one of the Owen House neighbors. It seems that women have been observed leaving the house at late hours. Do you have an explanation for this?"

"Yes, ma'am," I replied quickly. "Stevens House doesn't have enough women living there during the summer session to warrant cooking, so they take their meals over at Owen House and share the cooking and clean-up chores with the men."

"What time do you serve dinner?" Dean Barker asked.

"Six o'clock."

"Then why would women be seen leaving the house after nine p.m.?"

Gloria spoke for the first time. "With all respect, the women may stay out until ten-thirty without having to account for themselves."

"I'm well aware of that, Miss Greeley," Dean Barker said icily. "but it doesn't apply to women visiting in men's residences."

Gloria's eyebrows shot up. "Even if they're restricted to the ground floor? Is this another university *rule for women?*"

Dean Barker's expression grew colder. Pointing to Gloria's jeans, she said, "While we're on the subject of university rules, there's a rule prohibiting women from wearing clothing such as yours—blue jeans, pedal pushers, shorts—on campus."

"Why are there all these rules for women and not for *men?*" Gloria snapped. She angrily jabbed a finger at me. "Look at him. Obviously, the university doesn't tell *him* what to wear!"

I nervously fingered the frayed collar on my Sears Roebuck plaid shirt, wishing I was back at the house doing my fluid mechanics homework.

Dean Barker responded. "The men are not my responsibility, Miss Greeley, but the women *are.* I am accountable to the parents of every female student on campus. I have to assure them that their daughters will receive an education in a proper, wholesome, and virtuous environment."

Gloria rolled her eyes. "Dean Barker, this is nineteen fifty-four, not nineteen *oh* four! Isn't it time the universities started putting something else in a woman's head besides how to dress and act so she can snag some nincompoop engineer or doctor who's going to make a pile of money when he graduates?"

Nincompoop? I opened my mouth to voice an opinion on that last remark but thought better of it. My old man used to say—never get involved in a fight between two women.

They went back and forth for several minutes, but Dean Barker ran out of time before Gloria ran out of arguments. Barker regained her composure as she ushered us to the door.

"I appreciate that the Stevens House women need nutritious meals, but make certain that they leave Owen House no later than seven-thirty in the evening."

Anxious to leave, I nodded frantically in agreement. However, Gloria had to have the last word. "Someday, Dean Barker, men and women will be living *together* in university housing."

Dean Barker smiled patronizingly. "Not in our lifetime, Miss Greeley, not in our lifetime."

Turning to me, she said, "Mr. Harju, I expect you to enforce this. The women are to leave your house by seven-thirty."

Throw a bunch of women out of the house every night? The old man was right. Management was tricky.

Friday, August 13th, 1954
Owen House

The summer session was over. Today, the last day of finals, was a time for wild rejoicing, reckless goofiness, or just falling to your knees to thank the academic gods for allowing you to take yet another step toward your coveted college degree.

All hell was breaking loose at Owen House. In the living room a half-dozen guys were guzzling cold beer from quart bottles, one strumming a guitar and the rest belting out obscene verses of "Roll Your Leg Over." In the kitchen a normally mousy pre-med student from Stevens House—also more-than-somewhat beered up—was, just for the hell of it, mixing blue food coloring into the mashed potatoes for dinner. On the third floor, a couple of idiots were firing off cherry bombs left over from the Fourth of July.

I wanted to sit down with a cold beer and sing dirty songs too, but I had my hands full trying to keep a lid on the place. I yelled up the stairwell at the third-floor cherry bombers to knock it off. The last thing I needed during my final hours as house manager was to have some neighbor call the police about the noise and have the cops march in, wanting to check I.D.'s of the beer drinkers. I didn't know who was twenty-one and who wasn't.

I finally took refuge on the couch next to the only other person in the living room who I knew for certain was old enough to drink beer. This was Yudi Balzar, and he never touched the stuff.

Balzar was about thirty—much older than the rest of us—and had spent World War II in someone's army over in one of those Balkan countries.

With his enormous frame and heavy drooping mustache, he was the spitting image of a young Joe Stalin. He had arrived at Owen House in June, speaking very little English. All foreign students with limited English were required to attend an intensive English-language school, taught by the university, before being allowed to enroll in regular classes. Balzar had been there all summer.

Tonight, amid the raucous celebrating, Balzar was laboriously deciphering an article in *The Ann Arbor News* about an interstate highway system proposed by President Eisenhower. His mouth moved carefully over every word.

"Whut iz diz beerokrat?" he asked. Balzar had fallen in love with English and was forever pestering people for word definitions.

"Bureaucrats are what the United States government is made of, Yudi," I told him.

He nodded. "Whut iz putthole?"

"Potholes are what Eisenhower wants the bureaucrats to fill."

The cook hit the dinner buzzer, and everyone rushed to the dining-room door. Balzar and I brought up the rear.

Just then the two idiots on the third floor thought it would be a good time to light a cherry bomb and drop it down the stairwell. It almost reached the ground floor—but not quite. As we passed through the foyer, the cherry bomb exploded in midair with a horrific blast, about six inches from Balzar's head.

The firecrackers had been going off all afternoon, so everyone in the dining room just hooted and yelled goodnaturedly. But Balzar grabbed his ear and dropped to the floor, his face contorted in pain.

I knelt beside him. "Yudi, are you okay?"

He didn't reply but after several seconds got to his feet and slowly headed for the stairs.

I took his arm. "Maybe you'd better sit on the couch for a minute..."

Balzar violently jerked his arm away—totally out of character for him—and marched slowly up the stairs. He looked to be okay, so I let him go.

I went up to the third floor and gave the cherry bombers hell. However, a house manager didn't have the authority to dole out punishment. You had to *reason* with people, appealing to their common sense and innate intelligence. Naturally, the two cherry bombers only laughed at me.

I went back down the stairs. The door to Balzar's room on the second floor was closed. I figured that he wanted to lie down until his hearing returned, so I proceeded to the dining room to get some food before it was all gone.

Just as I was scooping some still-plentiful, beautiful bright blue mashed potatoes onto my plate, there was a loud commotion upstairs.

"HOUSE MANAGER!"
"HE'S GOT A KNIFE! HE'S GOT A KNIFE!"
"HOUSE MANAGER!"

I jumped up and dashed into the foyer, looking up the stairwell. Two frightened pairs of eyes were peering down from the third-floor landing at Balzar who was slowly climbing the stairs from the second floor—straight for them. A knife glinted in his hand.

I ran up the stairs, two at a time, not believing this. Balzar—the guy who never bitched about anything, always tolerating the horseplay around Owen House—was going after someone with a knife.

A door slammed violently, then sounds of furniture dragging on the floor. I reached the third-floor landing just as Balzar reared back and crashed one massive shoulder into the closed door of the cherry-bombers' room. He was grasping a long-bladed knife.

The door shuddered, but the two cherry bombers had pushed their desks up against it from the inside, and it held. Whimpers and grunts of exertion from within. More furniture was pulled across the floor and something—probably a dresser—was thrown on top of the desks holding the door closed.

I stood a respectful distance away. "Yudi, why don't you give me the knife?" I said quietly.

Balzar lifted up one leg and gave the door a thunderous kick. "Iz not knife. Iz... iz... a... whut you call it..."

I looked closely at the weapon. "A bayonet?"

Balzar flashed me a quick smile of gratitude. "Yas—yas... bah-yoo-nat. Thenk you." Concentrating again on the business at hand, he lifted his leg to chest level and kicked the door again. This time wood splintered.

"Yudi, if you murder those guys—and they deserve it, I know—you'll go to jail."

Balzar looked at the door closely, inspecting the damage so he could better aim his next kick. "No murder. Mebbe joost cut off ears so dey know how I feel after dey throw big... big..."

"Cherry bomb," I volunteered.

Balzar looked at me questioningly. "Cherry bum?"

"It's a big firecracker."

"Yas... yas... firecracker." He silently mouthed the word, filed it away for future reference, and then kicked the door a third time. It still held.

"Even if you just cut off their ears, at the very least you'll get deported back to your home and your police will throw you in jail. How will you be able to practice your English there? You'll forget it—a real shame."

Balzar kept staring at the door, but his black, bushy eyebrows furrowed in thought as he pondered what I'd just said. After a long minute, he turned suddenly and headed for the stairs. "Okay. Iz not worth lose Engliss."

"You made a wise decision, Yudi," I said.

Balzar stopped at the head of the stairs, held up the bayonet, and looked at me quizzically. "Whut iz Engliss wurd for diz ting again?"

It was after midnight when I finally fell into bed after doing my laundry, cleaning up my room, and packing for the trip to White Sands the next day. Of the original seven who had begun the work co-op program at White Sands Proving Ground, I was the only one who had signed up for a third term.

A Brush With Failure

White Sands Proving Ground
August 1954 - January 1955

Monday, August16th, 1954
Climatic Testing Laboratory
White Sands Proving Ground

"**S**he's a dandy, ain't she?" Flint exclaimed. I nodded enthusiastically, not because Flint was my boss but because he was right. It *was* a dandy.

Being back on the job was exciting. Flint had immediately taken me over to a huge tower near the Climatic Testing Lab. Constructed of steel I-beams, it rose sixty feet into the air. Inside the tower was a forty-eight-foot Viking rocket—not visible because it was completely enshrouded by the thermal jacket that Joe Raven and I had begun designing a year ago. Wires and pipes sprouted from the walls of the jacket, connecting the rocket inside to a variety of test instruments on the three platforms located along the perimeter of the tower.

It would look like a big thermos bottle, Joe Raven had said. And this morning—all assembled—it *did* look like a giant, shiny thermos bottle, the curved aluminum skin sharply reflecting the early morning sunlight.

"We took delivery on the jacket from the El Paso contractor only two weeks ago," Flint said, shielding his eyes from the sun as he continued gazing up at the tower. "Been putting the whole works together ever since—the missile, jacket, and test equipment. We'll start testing in two weeks."

"What kind of tests are you going to run?" I asked.

Flint looked at me with amusement. "You're the project engineer, remember? *You're* going to run the tests. Think you'll be ready to go in two weeks?"

"Will Joe Raven be working with me on this?"

"Nope. Raven got promoted to corporal and transferred out in May. Any GI worth a damn always gets promoted and transferred. But don't worry, you'll get all the help you need from others in the lab."

Inside the tower was a forty-eight-foot Viking rocket—not visible because it was completely enshrouded by the thermal jacket.

Back in the lab, not everyone was happy with Flint for picking a young puppy like me as the project engineer for this new job.

Eugene Grubb, a hulking, freckle-faced New Mexico A&M co-op student new to our lab, had been assigned to work for me. He didn't like the idea of taking orders from a fellow co-op student—*especially* one from *Michigan.*

Chewing on a toothpick, Grubb looked down at me disapprovingly. "How old're yew?"

"Twenty-one."

"Twenny-one? Sheet, *ah'll* be twenny-one in a munth, an' ah gotta work fer *yew*? Sheet!"

"If you think we won't get along," I replied diplomatically, "see Flint about getting another assignment. I don't mind."

"Ah kin git along with *anybody*," Grubb declared testily. He knew he wouldn't make a good impression on Flint if he bellyached about his first assignment.

Later I bumped into Bill Starzyk, also assigned to the Viking test. Two years earlier, as an electrician's apprentice, I had worked for Starzyk. Now the situation was reversed, and Starzyk didn't like it.

"How many thermocouples you gonna use on the rocket?" he asked sharply.

"I haven't had a chance to think about that, Bill."

"Ain't you looked at the missile schematic yet?"

"I've only been here two hours."

"Well, you're gonna need fifteen thermocouples for missile temperatures. I'll make 'em up tomorrow," he stated, setting the record straight as to who was the more qualified to make decisions.

Monday, September 20th, 1954
Viking Test Tower

At six p.m. I left the lab and went to the tower to supervise the start of another test. I had gone to the tower several times earlier in the day to check missile temperatures, the dry ice supply, and generally to make sure that everything was okay.

By now the project-engineer job had become fairly routine: scheduling, checking, and grinding out detailed test reports on the lab's ancient typewriter. But five weeks ago things had started at a breakneck pace. First, I had to take a self-imposed cram course on the Viking—not easy since a liquid-fuel rocket is a complex jungle of hardware and electrical wiring. I studied hard. At college, scoring an eighty-five percent on an engineering exam netted you a B+. When you tested rockets, however, there was no such thing as a B+. Anything less than one hundred percent was usually a failure—often catastrophic.

Everything had to be planned and scheduled. Were the temperature recorders, oscilloscopes, and test probes available, working, and calibrated? Was the Field All Temperature (FAT) unit ready to go? Could we depend on dry ice deliveries from El Paso? And most importantly, my test team. I had to line up people to run the test three shifts a day, seven days a week. By now I knew everyone's vacation plans for the rest of their lives. To a project engineer, the calendar was more important than his slide rule.

We were running long-term cold tests on the Viking's plumbing system. With all the valves, injectors, relays, pressure regulators, pipes, and electrical circuits, would the fuel and oxidizer actually get to the engine at sub-zero temperatures?

Twenty-four hours a day we pumped dry-ice-cooled air into the thermal jacket encasing the Viking. Over the weeks, we had driven the missile's temperature lower and lower, testing the plumbing system at increasingly colder temperature levels. Tonight we were going to attempt the test at the coldest temperature yet—thirty degrees below zero.

Twenty feet up on the side of the tower was an instrumentation room—really nothing more than a steel-plated compartment barely big enough for two guys to get into and still run the test equipment. We called it the "box." Tonight Eugene Grubb and Roger Olsen—a big Swede corporal who used to be a car mechanic in Minot, North Dakota—were taking the swing shift in the box.

I trotted up a flight of iron stairs leading to the box and stuck my head in. A few feet away, the Viking missile sitting in its thermal jacket may have been at minus thirty degrees, but the inside of the box was a sauna from the afternoon sun beating on the steel plating. Grubb and Olsen were crammed in like sardines and sweating profusely.

"Gawdam, Chief, it's hot in here! Didja bring cold beer?" Grubb said, mopping his face with a soggy handkerchief.

Grubb and I got along well now. It turned out that he didn't mind taking orders from me as long as the orders made sense.

"Did you pressurize the helium tank yet?" I asked. During flight, stored high-pressure helium pushed the liquid oxygen and fuel into the Viking's rocket engine for combustion. Our tests did the same thing without firing the engine, instead using an inert antifreeze mixture in the fuel and oxygen tanks.

"Not yet," Grubb replied. "We're gonna do it right now and then pressurize the liquid ox and fuel tanks with the helium. The test'll be ready t'go in 'bout half hour."

"Good. I'm going over at the NCO club to grab a bite to eat, but I'll be back by then. Close this door when you start pressurizing."

"You kiddin'? We close th'door an' we'll cook in here."

"The safety margin on those Viking tanks is too slim to screw around with," I explained.

I left the technical area and crossed the street to the NCO club. I normally ate meals over at the Officers' Club, but when we were running tests, the NCO club, within sight of the Viking test tower, was more convenient.

A corporal at the grill fried up a couple of greasy cheeseburgers for me. I wolfed them down and was just about to stick a fork in my apple pie ala mode when...

WWHHHUUU——-MMMPPP!!!

A sharp explosion shook the building. The apple pie ala mode danced away from my fork, flipping the scoop of ice cream into the air.

The corporal at the grill immediately hit the deck behind the counter. A couple of off-duty sergeants having an early-evening brew dove out of their chairs and swore loudly as they landed on the floor on top of their spilled beer. Everyone who worked at the proving ground was conditioned for disaster since explosions weren't uncommon at White Sands. But not right here at the base center where people ate, slept, and drank beer.

I immediately knew what had happened. I bounded for the door and got outside just as a piece of twisted metal dropped out of the sky, clanging to the asphalt. It was icy cold. I ran like hell for the tower.

The heavy, I-beam tower was still intact. So was the instrumentation room. But the Viking rocket, along with our thermal jacket, was gone.

Twisted pieces of aluminum, large tufts of asbestos insulation, splinters of wood, mangled piping, and bits of wiring were scattered over a considerable area. The FAT unit lay on its side on the concrete, spilling out fragments of steaming dry ice from a gaping hole. The whole place smelled like a brewery from all the antifreeze that had been in the Viking's tanks.

The siren on the roof of the fire station howled, and people came running from all directions.

I galloped up the metal staircase to the instrumentation room and jerked open the door.

The power was out and the air was heavy with the stench of burned wiring. Grubb and Olsen were sitting in the smoky gloom, dazed but alive.

"You guys okay?" I shouted.

Grubb was rubbing his ears. "Ya gotta speak up, Chief. Ah cain't hear a word you're sayin'"

I grabbed his arm and pulled him out into the fresh air. Olsen staggered out behind him.

They didn't appear to have any broken bones, but both men were badly shaken and neither could hear a thing. I couldn't even imagine what it must have sounded like in that cramped metal room only a few feet from a large exploding rocket. They were lucky. Minutes before, they had been bitching about the temperature inside the room, but the heavy steel-plated walls responsible for the heat had saved their lives.

The explosion shot most of the missile and the thermal jacket up through the open top of the tower. One hundred and fifty yards away, the Viking's large liquid oxygen tank had landed intact on a big missile-assembly building and was firmly imbedded in the roof—half in and half out.

Moments before, this had been the first engineering project I had ever managed. Now it was scattered junk.

A couple of firemen charged up the staircase, but there wasn't room for all of us on the tower, so I made my way down and let them go up to examine Grubb and Olsen.

The firemen quickly released Grubb and Olsen, and they came down the tower staircase.

"Chief, ah could sure use a cold beer," Grubb said to me, twisting his head around to loosen his neck muscles.

Olsen still couldn't hear and continued to vibrate like a tuning fork. "W-what'd you s-say?" he yelled, digging into his ear with a grimy finger.

"AH SAID COLD BEER!" Grubb yelled back.

Olsen nodded vigorously.

For all I knew, the Military Police were going to appear at any moment, wanting to know who was responsible for all this. "Nobody's drinking beer," I decreed.

"But today's mah birthday," Grubb pleaded. "Ah'm twenny-one."

"Happy birthday," I muttered morosely.

Crowds of GI's and civilians were now at the scene, excitedly picking fragments off the ground only to drop the metal ones that were still too cold to handle.

One irate sergeant muttered, "How th'hell come they let people run missile tests right here within spitting distance of the NCO Club?"

It was a very good question. I didn't know the answer.

Tuesday, September 21st, 1954
White Sands Headquarters Building
General Ely's Office

"**W**ho in the gawdamn hell gave you permission to test rockets right next to the main street of this base?" General Ely bellowed at the Range Safety Officer, Flint, and me as we stood on the carpet in his office the next morning.

Army Brigadier General Harold Ely, commander of White Sands Proving Ground, hated explosions. He had to explain them to his superiors in Washington, and this took time and paperwork. And there were plenty of explosions at White Sands in the 1950's. Rockets exploded in mid-trajectory, well before they reached their assigned destinations. Others barely lifted off the launch pad before they blew to smithereens. Some merely toppled over at X-minus zero and with the engine blasting at full throttle, skittered crazily across the concrete launch pad, finally exploding. Other misguided missiles slithered and bounced miraculously through the sandy boondocks for a mile or more, leaping over Highway US-70 at very low altitudes before blowing up. Needless to say, this did little to promote the tourist trade in New Mexico at the time.

"I'm waiting for an answer," the general growled.

"Sir, we've been testing missile subsystems in that tower for years," the Range Safety Officer replied nervously. "It's more economical than trans-porting personnel and heavy equipment out to the launch complex. Your predecessor deemed it safe as long as the missiles weren't fueled."

The general impatiently waved off the explanation. "That policy will undergo immediate reevaluation. Now, just exactly what th'hell happened last night?"

Flint spoke up. "Sir, let Mr. Harju, my project engineer, provide the technical details."

I was jarred into full alert. Since Flint had been fully briefed on the incident, I assumed that he would do all the talking. I couldn't believe he was shifting it off to me.

General Ely eyed my suspiciously. "Project engineer? How old are you, son?"

"Twenty-one, sir."

"I know that rocket science is in its infancy, but I had no idea to what extent. Okay, project engineer, let's have it."

The only generals I had ever seen up close were in the movies. Now I had to explain to a real live one why an expensive project that I was in charge of blew up within a five-iron shot of his office.

I stood at attention, hands ready to grab my legs in case they buckled, and nervously cleared my throat.

"Fortunately sir, the tower instrumentation room, with its two occupants and all the recording devices, survived the blast in good shape. Last night we examined the data readout from the charts. It seems that the Viking's main pressure regulator failed while pressurizing the fuel and liquid oxygen tanks. The tank pressures exceeded their prescribed limits and the fuel tank burst."

"Burst?" the general fumed. "A nice way of saying it blew all t'hell, isn't it?"

"Well... yessir. The regulator probably froze up since the temperature we were testing the system at was thirty below zero."

"Thirty below zero?" the general roared. "We don't fire rockets at thirty below zero! This is *New Mexico*, boy! It never gets that cold around here! What the hell were you people thinking of?"

Flint and I didn't receive our paychecks from the army, but the army controlled every activity at the proving ground, and I could see that we were in big trouble. I was about to become the only engineering student in the history of the University of Michigan to be court-martialed before graduation.

At that point Flint jumped in. "Sir, the explosion was an unfortunate accident—luckily no one was injured. But consider this: components like this faulty pressure regulator are presently found in every liquid-fuel rocket in this country's inventory. If we can't rely on our rockets in adverse climates, the United States will be extremely handicapped in future applications—space research and military.

"So the information gathered yesterday is invaluable. These regulators can be replaced or modified at a small cost. The Viking and other rockets will become much more reliable vehicles in the future."

Flint dropped his voice to a confidential level. "Besides, sir, the Viking is a navy research rocket, under the jurisdiction of our good Commander Berkley here at the proving ground."

He leaned over the general's desk like they were old friends. "Wouldn't it be an interesting topic of conversation over Thanksgiving Day cocktails at the Officers' Club, during the Army-Navy game, that you discovered a weakness in one of the navy's rockets?"

The Range Safety Officer—an army major—strangled a laugh.

General Ely listened intently, digesting the information. After a long moment he got up from his chair, a signal that the meeting was at an end.

"Gentlemen, we'll consider this event a learning experience, but under no circumstance will there be any future rocket testing of that nature, except out at the blockhouse." The general scowled menacingly. "Is that clear?"

We nodded enthusiastically and left. General Ely's directive would be easy enough to follow since the Viking and all our test equipment were in a million pieces.

As we left the Headquarters Building, I asked Flint why he had tapped me to explain the explosion to the general.

Flint grinned. "You were clearly depressed, and I wanted to take your mind off your troubles." Then he added, "Don't let this get you down. Everyone has failures—especially around here. The important thing is to learn from the experience.

Flint dismissed the whole topic with a wave of his hand. "Now that you've got some free time, we've got this Nike Hercules heat-cycle test ready to start next week..."

Tuesday, November 23rd, 1954
White Sands Proving Ground

Today I received a fat envelope from the College of Engineering at Michigan. I knew what it was—spring-semester registration forms—so I didn't bother to open it right away. Later in the BOQ I discovered a letter inside as well.

Dear Mr. Harju:

Enclosed are the College of Engineering registration forms for the spring semester. Please complete them at your earliest convenience and return to this office. Class registration begins in the Waterman Gymnasium on 1 February 1955.

As you must know, due to your participation in the White Sands Cooperative Program, your graduation date will no longer be 1955. For purposes of internal bookkeeping, The College of Engineering has reclassified you to the Class of 1957. This graduation date may be subject to further adjustment should you continue in the cooperative program.

> *Yours truly,*
> *Emily Maxwell*
> *Secretary to the Assistant Dean*

I grabbed my slide rule and whipped out one of my new ball-point pens (I now carried three at all times—blue, black, and red) from my plastic pocket protector and did a quick calculation on the back of the envelope. Emily Maxwell was right. I couldn't graduate before the spring semester in 1957 and then only if I dropped the White Sands program after this tour of duty. If not, it would be '58 or '59 before I got my diploma.

My gawd, I thought, guys I ran around with at the West Quad when we were all freshmen—Dick Beaudry, Murray Rosenkranz, Bubba Tibodeaux, and the rest—would be graduating this next year. I still had sixty credit hours left. That was *two full years.*

I always knew that working at the proving ground every fall was delaying graduation, but I put off thinking about it. I really didn't want to drop the program.

I *liked* White Sands. A chill went down my spine every time the ground shook at the blockhouse as a rocket was being launched. Every day was a fresh adventure. It was as exciting as the Fourth of July, except the firecrackers were bigger.

I had been devastated by the Viking explosion, but Flint immediately reassigned me, and within days I was fully engrossed scheduling people and equipment on a new project. I still had a lot to learn about engineering, but in rocket technology so did everyone else. No one here was overly critical if you made mistakes because *everyone* here made mistakes. You tried something—if it didn't work, you swept the debris aside, got out your slide rule, recalculated, scratched your head, and tried something else.

But I also wanted to get my engineering degree, and it was going to take forever at this rate.

Friday, January 28th, 1955
The Gila Monster Bar and Grill
Organ, New Mexico

Inflation had hit hard at the Gila Monster Bar and Grill during the past year. The price of a chili and cheeseburger deluxe combo had shot up from thirty-five cents to forty-five. No matter, I was now a GS-4, making a buck sixty an hour and could well afford it.

On the last Friday before my return to Michigan, Flint and I again had a farewell dinner together, but this time I was picking up the tab. I had something to tell him.

Over our Miller High Lifes, I brought it up.

"I'm not coming back next August."

Flint stared at me hard but didn't say anything.

I continued. "It's taking me forever to get through school. I've got to start piling up credits faster by spending both semesters in Ann Arbor. Even at that, I won't be getting my degree till 1957."

"You know you'll have a job waiting for you when you get through," he said earnestly. "If you want it."

I nodded my head, feeling the emotion welling up inside. "Am I doing the right thing?"

Flint took a long sip of beer and stared out the window. "I'm really tempted to say no, to tell you to stay with the program a little longer—I can use you. But I'd be doing you a disservice. As an undergraduate, you've gone about as far as you can here—actually further than most. With an engineering degree, you'll have a great future at White Sands. Go back to Michigan and finish up as quickly as you can. White Sands will still be here."

It was dark by the time Flint and I finished our chili and cheeseburgers. As we drove back over San Augustin Pass, we could see the puddle of lights ahead of us from the proving ground five miles away.

"Kinda pretty at night, ain't it?" Flint said, downshifting his '48 Ford on the grade to save the brakes.

"Yeah," I said, blinking back a tear.

Damn... what was wrong with me tonight? I was getting choked up about a place where armed M.P.'s checked your identification at the gate and placed you under martial law once you drove inside. Where roadblocks were put up across the highway for hours on end so civilians' cars wouldn't get impaled by errant rockets. Where only coyotes, rattlesnakes, gila monsters, and tarantulas wanted to live in the hundred-and-twenty-degree summer heat, and savage sandstorms blasted the paint off your car in the winter.

But I'd be back. Someday I'd be back.

Final Examinations

THE UNIVERSITY OF MICHIGAN
SEPTEMBER 1956 - MAY 1957

Tuesday, September 4th, 1956
Republic, Michigan

The old man poured steaming coffee from the chipped cup into the saucer to cool it off. With rock-steady fingertips he quickly and expertly hoisted the brimming saucer to his lips and took a noisy slurp. He had been drinking coffee this way ever since I could remember.

We sat at the oilcloth-covered kitchen table while my mother fried breakfast eggs and bacon in a big black frying pan on the wood stove. I'd arrived in Republic the night before, having driven practically non-stop from California, where I'd worked during the summer, to Upper Michigan to spend a few days at home before the fall semester began.

"So what subjeks you takin' this time?" The old man didn't know anything about engineering courses but always asked that same question. My answers convinced him that college was making me smarter.

I mentally reviewed my fall course schedule. "Let's see... a course on those new analog computers, theory of elasticity, photoelasticity, dynamic responses, advanced fluid mechanics, and principles of gyroscopes."

The old man nodded and grunted with satisfaction.

"How was your summer job?" my mother asked.

"Okay. Nothing special."

Without the White Sands cooperative program, I needed some income, so I took student-engineering positions at aircraft companies in Southern California during the summers of '55 and '56.

I hated those jobs. Eight hours a day in a hanger-sized room, being a glorified draftsman alongside hundreds of other faceless engineers, tinkering with the design of some little nut-and-bolt assembly that would be inserted into a very large airplane.

But the money was good. This summer Douglas Aircraft had paid me an amazing three hundred and ninety-two dollars a month, allowing me to cover college expenses and pick up a nice 1950 Chevrolet in the bargain. It wasn't the new Buick with the automatic transmission I'd lusted after years ago, but it got me around.

"Tha' new car a yers give ya any trouble?" In the old man's mind, any car less than ten years old was new.

"Nope. Ran out of gas in Hershey, Nebraska, in the middle of the night. I just slept in the backseat till the town's gas station opened."

"When ya gotta be in Ann Arbor?"

"Sunday night, for the semester job-election meeting at Owen House. Since I was house manager last spring, I have to run the meeting."

"This yer last semester, huh?"

"Yeah. I graduate in February, and then I'm off to White Sands to work for Mr. Flint."

"I never can remember what kind of engineer you're going to be," my mother said.

"Engineering mechanics—not the same as mechanical engineering."

Both of them registered blank looks.

"Engineering mechanics is the study of forces on bodies," I explained. "I'm taking it with an aeronautical minor to get the best background I can for rocket work."

"When all the relatives come over for coffee Thursday night, could you explain that to your Uncle Hugo?" my mother asked. "He's always asking me what you're going to be."

She put heaping plates of bacon and eggs down in front of the old man and me. My visit must have been a monumental occasion. She was using her good Jewel Tea dishes to serve breakfast.

Wednesday, September 12th, 1956
Waterman Gymnasium

The class-registration process in Waterman Gym hadn't changed much in five years. I navigated around long lines and successfully avoided the crush of flailing arms and elbows, making my way to the "Engineering Mechanics" table. It was manned by Professor Oliver Thurnby, head of the department. There was no line here. Few understood engineering mechanics well enough to want a degree in it.

Thurnby quickly made out my class schedule and proceeded to go over it with me. "Pretty cushy, hey?" he declared jovially. "No eight o'clocks and only *two* nine o'clocks. We try to keep our seniors happy, heh, heh."

No such thing, of course. The advanced courses I was now taking were taught only by the most eminent engineering professors who didn't like eight o'clocks any more than the students.

And there was nothing cushy about my class load. Six courses would keep me hopping.

"You *are* thinking about grad school, aren't you?" Thurnby asked. "Go on for a master's in engineering mechanics after you get your bachelor's in February?"

"Uh... no, sir. I'll be getting a job right away."

"A master's degree would look impressive on future resumes."

"I won't need a resume, sir. I've already got a position lined up working for the government at White Sands Proving Ground."

Thurnby raised his eyebrows. "Civil Service? You can do much better than that. Every company in the country is begging for engineers right now. And a Michigan engineer with a master's degree would command a salary *twice* the amount you'd get in a Civil Service job."

I was growing uncomfortable with the conversation. "White Sands is really where I want to work, sir. The salary isn't really all that important."

Thurnby didn't understand that. "I'd like to see you reconsider. This afternoon I'm having some department faculty members and graduate students over to my place for refreshments—a little social get-together before we roll up our sleeves for the semester. Stop by and chat with some of these people. You may have second thoughts."

201

For engineers, it was strictly a formal affair—tweed sports coats with leather elbow patches. I didn't have one and felt conspicuous.

The air in Professor Thurnby's parlor was thick with assorted blends of pipe-tobacco smoke as the scholarly gathering conversed in sentences filled with equations and Greek letters.

At the refreshment table, two different wines—white and red—were available, accompanied by Mrs. Thurnby's creations: small crustless white bread sandwiches filled with a thin, unidentifiable spread and fastened together with frilled toothpicks.

Recalling that liver and onions—something I really disliked—was being served at Owen House that night, I stuffed several of the sandwiches into my mouth and washed them down with the white wine. I immediately recognized the wine from the co-op hootenany parties: a local blend made in Hamtramack, Michigan, available in all retail stores for a dollar forty-five a gallon.

"Welcome to our group."

Terence Sproon, a tall, skinny engineering mechanics doctoral candidate, was talking to me. I'd seen Sproon around, but we had never spoken.

Sproon's eyes looked tiny behind his extremely thick glasses. He delicately sipped his Hamtramack white wine, pressing his lips together, savoring the vintage.

"I'm sure you will enjoy these little get-togethers," he added in a high-toned voice. "Discussing one anothers' theses over a glass of wine can be most stimulating." He didn't sound like an engineer at all.

"I'm just getting my bachelor's degree," I said. "I don't have a thesis."

"Of course, of course, but you'll be giving it some thought before long. Thurnby will see to that."

"He will?"

Sproon smiled enigmatically. "Dr. Thurnby looks at each engineering mechanics graduate as a potential faculty member. For that you need the doctorate. Trust me, before the semester is over Thurnby will be approaching you, asking you to consider a thesis topic, just as he did with me seven years ago."

"You've been in graduate school for *seven years*?"

"Yes, I turned thirty last month. But a most exciting seven years it's been. Researching a fascinating subject like mine has a way of making time fly."

"What's your thesis?"

His small eyes gleamed with pride at the question. "'The Effects of Buckling on the Resonant Frequency of Uni-metal, Thin-Shelled Parabaloids,'" he announced. "It was my own idea," he added modestly.

For the next ten minutes, Sproon rattled on about his thesis. I understood none of it.

"What's the application?" I finally asked.

Sproon looked puzzled. "Application?"

"What will the results of your thesis be used for?"

"Oh... I don't have the time to concern myself with applications. I'll leave that to others, like Thurnby. Too many things to do. Why, during this coming year alone, I'll be delivering papers at four different conferences. Foreign travel too: the one in April is in Saskatoon, Saskatchewan.

"Then, in a few years—after the doctorate, of course—I'll be eligible for an assistant professorship..." He paused dramatically. "And finally, a full professorship *with lifetime tenure!*" Sproon folded his spindly arms and smiled broadly, confident that his career plans had me overwhelmed.

I'd seen plenty of engineering-faculty offices tucked away in remote recesses of the West and East Engineering buildings—awful little rooms with paint peeling off the walls, crowded with rickety furniture and towering stacks of blue books filled with disorganized, illegible equations that had to be graded for accuracy.

I finished the wine and edged toward the refreshment table, using my empty glass as an excuse to get away from Sproon.

Seven years—jeezuz!

Thursday, December 6th, 1956
West Engineering Building

Wanda Pringle, a student in my principles of gyroscopes class, was like the rest of the small core of female engineers at Michigan—bright as hell. From time to time she would stand around with the professor after class challenging his lecture statements on Routhian procedure, skew symmetry, and other gyroscopic miscellany. This kind of talent mystified me. I had all I could do to drill the stuff into my brain in the solitude of my little basement room at Owen House.

This morning I was completely surprised when after class, Wanda approached me instead of the professor.

"Today is my twenty-first birthday," she opened bluntly. "A bunch of my friends and I are going down to the P-Bell tonight to celebrate. Want to come along?"

Wanda wasn't half-bad looking, something you wouldn't expect in a woman taking such a heavyweight course as principles of gyroscopes. It had been a long time since I'd had a date, and who knows—she might turn out to be a hot tamale.

I declined. "Gee, thanks Wanda, I'd like to but I've got an elasticity blue book tomorrow, and I'd better hit the books tonight."

She shrugged with a half smile and wandered off.

The real reason I didn't want to go was I'd become so focussed on school this semester that I'd gotten out of the habit of dating, beer drinking, and all the other extracurricular vices. Day in and day out I climbed out of bed, went to classes, came back to Owen House, ate, and studied. I was content with this monkish existence because graduation and returning permanently to White Sands were powerful incentives.

I was trudging off toward my next class in West Engineering, trying to rationalize the wisdom of not going beer drinking with Wanda, when I ran into Dean Emmert in the hallway.

"You're graduating in February, aren't you?" Emmert said.

"Yes, sir. I'll be heading back to White Sands to a full-time job."

"I see. And what GS rating did they offer you?"

"Oh... well actually, sir, it's been some time since I've contacted my boss, Mr. Flint."

Emmert looked surprised. "You're graduating in two months and you don't have a job nailed down?"

"Mr. Flint told me I'd have a job with him whenever I graduate."

"Flint's just a technical supervisor. Have you forgotten how slowly the government's bureaucratic wheels can turn? I'd advise you to contact them as soon as possible to get the paperwork started."

Taking Emmert's advice, I went down to the Blue Front News Stand that afternoon and made a call to White Sands Proving Ground.

A woman whose voice I didn't recognize answered the phone. "Good afternoon, Environmental Testing Facility."

"Oh, I must have the wrong number. I was trying to reach the Climatic Test Lab."

"This is the right number, sir. That laboratory is a part of the Environmental Testing Facility."

"Oh, I see. Then I wish to speak to Mr. Robert Flint."

"I'm sorry, there is no Mr. Flint at this number."

I spoke louder. "ARE YOU SURE I HAVE THE RIGHT NUMBER? I WANT TO SPEAK TO BOB FLINT OF THE CLIMATIC TEST LAB."

A pause. "Perhaps you should speak to my supervisor," she said. "Please hold a moment."

"Hello, this is Frank Merriwell—the director of Environmental Testing. Can I help you?"

"I'm trying to contact Mr. Bob Flint, head of the Climatic Test Lab. The woman said there's no Mr. Flint at this number."

"Ah, yes. The secretary is new and didn't know Mr. Flint. He's been gone for over a year—left shortly after the reorganization."

"Reorganization?" A cold knot settled in the pit of my stomach.

"Climatic Testing was one of several departments that became our new Environmental Testing Facility over a year ago."

I began speaking rapidly. "I was one of Mr. Flint's engineering co-op students for three years. I'll be graduating from the University of Michigan in February, and he promised me a job whenever I got out of school."

A pause. "I see. Well, that's a problem. When those smaller labs merged into one large organization, there were so many overlapping positions that we actually had to reassign engineers to other areas at the proving ground. I'm afraid we're not hiring right now. In fact, there's a hiring freeze in the whole Civil Service sector down here.

"Now, if you like, I can have an employment application sent to you to fill out and we'll contact you whenever the hiring picture changes."

The operator cut in. "Your thu-ree minutes are up. Pu-lease deposit sixty cents for another thu-ree minutes."

I mumbled a thank-you to the director of the new Environmental Testing Facility and hung up. Any further conversation wouldn't have been worth another sixty cents.

I hoisted my first glass of beer of the semester and emptied it in four swallows. It was an hour after the disastrous White Sands phone call, and I had talked Kozlovich into coming down to the P-Bell to keep me company. I polished off a second glass just as quickly.

"You drink yoost like Roossian today," Kozlovich remarked.

I smacked the empty glass on the table. "Five years... five years getting backaches leaning over drafting tables, breaking steel doohickeys with monster lab machines... five years wrestling with those stupid Greek equations and cramming for blue books... five years, and the only place where I really want to work can't hire me."

I told Kozlovich about the phone call and the fact that I was graduating in two months and didn't have a job.

"How about big Kulifornya airplane kumpanies you vurk at in summers?"

I poured out a third glass and shook my head. "Oh no... nooo thanks! Do you know how many engineers those companies put in one room? Hundreds... thousands. Room's so big you can hardly see the opposite wall on a smoggy day. It takes you a month to find your desk. You gotta punch a time clock every time you go in and out. Nooo thanks!"

Kozlovich took a thoughtful sip of beer and gazed at the P-Bell ceiling. "If I was engineer, I go to Kulifornya anyhow. Find rich movie star like Jane Roosell and get married."

We sat and drank beer awhile. Gradually my mood improved—amazing how that'll happen after you've had five or six.

"Boris, maybe I'll become a professional student."

Kozlovich was watching some fraternity chug-a-luggers two tables away, idly wondering if he should go over and hustle them. "Vut iss professnal student?"

"Remember that guy Sproon I told you about? He's a professional student. Thirty years old and dinking around with some obscure crap about buckling thin-shelled paraboloids that nobody understands or cares about. His only goal—if he even has one—is to get a Ph.D. so he can become a professor and spend the rest of his life scaring the hell out of undergraduate engineers with impossible exam questions.

"Maybe *I* should do something like that for a few years. Think about it... I could sign up for grad school... live cheap at the co-op house... come and go whenever I want... get my master's... do a little work on some hopeless thesis topic... get myself one of those sports coats with the leather elbow patches and go over to Thurnby's once in awhile and drink Hamtramack wine while I discuss plasticity theory with the rest of them."

"Girls luff grad students," Kozlovich added.

Suddenly I remembered that Wanda Pringle was coming to the P-Bell tonight. I stood up and gazed around the smoke-filled room. She wasn't here yet.

I should have been back in my room studying for tomorrow's elasticity blue book. Instead, I poured another glass of beer and stood up again to look around for Wanda.

Saturday, January 26th, 1957
Owen House

*L*ast week I'd completed my final undergraduate semester. Today my diploma arrived in the morning mail. Normally, the university sent diplomas to the graduate's home address, but since I wasn't leaving Ann Arbor, I'd notified them to send mine to Owen House.

The plain brown envelope wasn't very big—only six by eight inches. I opened it and casually glanced at the diploma. I was now officially an engineer.

During all my years at Michigan, I'd pictured graduation as being a big event. First, the ceremony here on campus and then back home with all the relatives coming over to the house to shake my hand and partake of the huge spread of food that my mother would have laid out on the long library table in the living room. But now I wasn't sure if anyone except my parents even knew I'd graduated.

It didn't matter. I was now totally indifferent about the whole thing. Earlier in the month, when I'd received a letter giving me instructions for attending the graduation ceremony, I didn't bother to reply. Without the job at White Sands that I'd had my heart set on, the degree seemed meaningless.

In two days I was going to enroll in grad school. I had soberly reassessed the idea after that night of beer drinking with Kozlovich at the P-Bell, and until I could restructure my future it was still the only plan that made any sense. At least Professor Thurnby would be pleased.

I took my diploma down to my room, stuck it away, and thought no more about it.

Thursday, April 25th, 1957
General Motors Research Facility
Warren, Michigan

*T*hree engineers and a personnel representative spent the entire morning giving me a tour of the General Motors Research Facility. Now, after the most elaborate free lunch I'd ever eaten, we all sat around a long oval table in an elegant conference room furnished with heavy pastel drapes and huge abstract paintings on burlap-covered walls.

The middle-aged personnel man pressed on with a lengthy sales pitch directed at me. His pink jowls flapped excitedly as he moved into his concluding remarks.

"Over the past decade we've consistently led Ford and Chrysler in every aspect of advanced engineering research, ranging from power train, electrical, fuel flow, steering, suspension, and aerodynamic body design. The exciting 1958 General Motors line will reflect the expertise of our brilliant engineering staff..."

I really tried to appear bright-eyed and alert, but his spiel dragged on like a long TV commercial and my mind kept drifting off. I began thinking about everything that had happened in the past three months.

On January 28th I had enrolled in Michigan's Horace H. Rackham School of Graduate Studies. Professor Thurnby helped choose my first-semester courses: plasticity theory, advanced dynamics, Fourier series, and aeroelasticity. Five years ago, just the names alone would have scared the hell out of me.

Over the weeks that followed, I nestled into a lackadaisical, yet very comfortable, routine. Each class had only a handful of students, and everyone received unlimited personal attention from friendly professors keen on swelling the ranks of graduate students. Quite the opposite treatment compared to my freshman year.

I put in just enough time on course work to get by, drank beer on weekends, and dated co-op girls. Kozlovich was right—grad students were popular with women.

It was a good life. I was beginning to see how Sproon had slipped into his seven-year graduate-school interlude. It was so easy that I seldom gave any thought to a permanent job these days.

Except there *was* this one problem—I was running out of money. If I planned to stay in school, I had to get a summer job.

On the bulletin board in West Engineering, I found an attractive offer. General Motors was willing to pay a stipend to grad-student engineers while attending school and give them a full-time job in the summer. It was perfect—enough money to get me through, and Warren, though forty miles from Ann Arbor, was still close enough to commute from Owen House.

I applied, and General Motors arranged the interview for today.

"Do you have any questions, sir?" The personnel man was looking at me.

My mind snapped back to the present. "Ah... yes... could you tell me what I'll be doing while I'm working here this summer?"

One of the engineers spoke up. "The 1960 Cadillac is on the drawing board, and the vibration characteristics of the hood have to be analyzed at high speed with necessary bracing designed to damp out any excess. It would be a perfect assignment for someone with your background. An exciting opportunity for you."

"Yes... exciting," I replied. *Analyze the hood of a car? Well... the money was good.*

The interview was concluded and the foursome escorted me to the main lobby. I was handed paperwork with instructions to fill it out as soon as possible.

The personnel man said, "We at General Motors like to think we're making an investment in the future. Can we assume that you would be coming here to work full time when you get your advanced degree?"

I took in the contemporary design of the lobby with its glass walls, plush carpeting, and a receptionist desk so big that an airplane could land on it. Certainly the most luxurious layout I'd ever seen. What engineer wouldn't jump at the chance?

"Well... I haven't exactly made up my mind yet... I'm still..."

That wasn't what he wanted to hear. "Come, come," he interrupted chidingly. "As a graduate student, you must have given your engineering career some serious thought. Truthfully now, what are your technical interests?"

Without thinking, I said, "I'd like to work with rockets."

The engineers looked astonished. The personnel man yelped, "Rockets?"

I cursed myself all the way back to Ann Arbor. What the hell was the matter with me—mentioning rockets to a bunch of automotive engineers. What was I thinking when I blurted that out? How dumb can you get?

From their reaction, it was clear that any chance of getting a job at General Motors had just gone down the drain.

The tranquil shell I'd lived in for the past three months had suddenly shattered. I was feeling extremely edgy not knowing how I was going to make ends meet in the coming months. After dinner, maybe Kozlovich would join me at the P-Bell for a few cold ones. That is, if he was willing to buy the beer.

I was in my room, nurturing my black mood as I struggled to undo the stubborn knot in my necktie, when someone yelled down the stairway saying that I had a phone call.

I picked up the phone in the foyer.

"Is this Mr. Harju?" a voice said faintly.

It sounded like long distance. "Yes," I replied, pressing a finger against my open ear and speaking loudly.

"My name is Edgar Poole from Douglas Aircraft."

Uh oh. They'd heard I'd graduated and wanted to know why I hadn't applied for a full-time job since they had been kind enough to give me a summer job last year.

I had to get rid of this guy fast. It was almost dinnertime and pork chops were being served. You were never late for pork-chop dinners at a co-op house.

He continued. "I'm calling from White Sands Proving Ground."

I froze, my hand still clutching the necktie knot. "White Sands? You're not in California?"

"No. As I think you know, Douglas Aircraft builds the Nike Ajax and Hercules missiles and tests them here at the proving ground. I'm in charge of Douglas's ground test equipment—mainly the rocket launchers.

The missile contractors! Why didn't I think of the missile contractors?

Poole continued. "I spoke to Bill Starzyk over at the Officer's Club yesterday. He mentioned your name and your experience at the old Climatic Test Lab. He thought you'd be graduating about now."

"I got my degree in February. I'm in graduate school now."

"Starzyk said you'd worked with Nike rockets. Is that true?"

"Yessir." *Has he got a job for me? Ohmigawd—ohmigawd—ohmigawd...*

"We have a new version of the Nike now, replaces the Ajax. It's called the Hercules."

"Yessir, I know. I was involved in temperature testing of the early Hercules model." *Gettothepoint—gettothepoint—please gettothepoint...*

He paused. "I need an engineer to manage modifications to the launchers. Starzyk thought you might be a good candidate."

I gripped the phone receiver hard. "Can... can you tell me a little bit about the job?"

"The Nike testing program not only evaluates and incorporates design changes to the rocket but also its launcher. You would be responsible for designing modifications to the launchers, drafting them, and going out to the launch area to supervise their implementation.

"I should point out that this isn't a nice desk job that many engineers prefer these days. You would be spending a lot of time out in the field at the launch site. How does that strike you?"

Is he kidding? "That's just fine, sir."

"But you just started grad school, and I need someone right away."

I thought furiously but only for about three seconds. "When do you want me to start?"

He laughed. "You'll have to fill out a job application first, and then of course, there's a little matter of discussing salary."

"Oh... yes... of course, sir."

Just then the Owen House cook hit the dinner buzzer and the house shook as everyone trampled their way to pork chops in the dining room. Kozlovich braked to a stop next to me and motioned violently toward the dining-room door. I shook my head. I didn't give a damn about pork chops.

Ten minutes later I hurriedly clinked two quarters and a dime into the Blue Front News Stand pay phone and dialed home.

"Hi, Pop. It's me."

"Anythin' wrong?"

"Not really, but I'm wondering... ah... could you lend me some money?" It wasn't an easy question to ask. I'd been self-sufficient since my freshman year.

"How much?"

"About a hundred dollars."

The old man didn't say anything for several seconds. "I'll haf'ta go to Ishpeming to the telegraph office t'wire it to ya."

"I'm taking a job at White Sands next month, and I need it to live on until I get my first paycheck."

"I thought you couldn't find work down there."

"A guy called and offered me a job. Sounds good."

"Whut happen t'grad school?"

"I'm gonna quit."

"Oh."

"Pop?"

"Whut?"

"Do you think I'm doing the right thing—quitting grad school?" I dreaded hearing his answer after all the pressure he and my mother had put on me to go to college.

A pause. "How old're you now—twenny-four?"

"Yeah."

"When you wuz a kid and didn't know nuthin', ya never asked fer advice. Now when yer old 'nough to know whut's whut, ya start askin'... I dunno...

"Th'way I figgur it, ya already got ten more grades a schoolin' than me. Are ya still gettin' smarter with this grad school?"

I shrugged at the telephone. "I don't know."

"Ya want this job?"

"Very much. I'm just thinking about the money I spent this semester... and the good grades I'm getting... and what Professor Thurnby will think..."

"Lemme ask ya sumthin'."

"What's that?"

"Will they ever tell ya yer too old t'go t'school?"

"What? No, I suppose not."

"Then at the pay ya'll be gettin', y'kin afford t'go back any time ya want. Take th'job."

It was the first time in recent memory that I wanted to hug the old man.

"Your thu-ree minutes are up. Pu-lease deposit sixty cents for another thu-ree minutes."

I hastily shoved in two more quarters and a dime, hoping the old man might have another pearl of wisdom. He did.

"An' another thing, ya probly wouldn' haf'ta borrow money if ya didn't keep makin' these damned telephone calls alla time."

Over my college years, I'd amassed quite a collection of long-playing records. Recently, on Friday nights, a bunch of us—including women from Stevens House—would cram into my basement room to celebrate the weekend over quarts of Stroh's beer. I would start off by playing Harry Belefonte, then, after a few beers, shock the group with Tom Lehrer's outrageous, iconoclastic ballads.

But when I was alone and wanted to think, I preferred classical music. Tonight, *Dvorak's New World Symphony* seemed to fit.

After starting the record I decided to search for my diploma. It was up on one of the top shelves, jammed between my freshman chemistry and principles of economics textbooks.

The dark blue imitation-leather cover was embossed with "University of Michigan" in gold lettering. Inside, the fancy Gothic print reflected the fancy words, certifying that upon recommendation of the College of Engineering, the regents of the University of Michigan had conferred upon me the degree of Bachelor of Science in Engineering with all the rights, privileges, and honors. Dated February second, nineteen hundred and fifty-seven and signed by Harlan Hatcher, president of the university.

For the first time since graduation I felt a deep sense of pride. Michigan was one of the toughest, most highly ranked engineering schools in the world, and there were many times that I was certain I'd never make it.

I gazed around the basement room. In recognition of my co-op seniority, I had it all to myself now. The first time I saw it years ago I thought it was the worst hole imaginable, but now it was fixed up just the way I wanted. Lots of wall shelving held my textbooks. I had long ago given up selling them to the bookstores at the end of the semester. They were badges of accomplishment to be kept forever. My old drafting equipment—the long T-square, plastic triangles, and French curves—was arranged and balanced like mobiles, hanging by wires from the water pipes running along the ceiling.

I had fashioned a life at Michigan that was now pulling at me irresistibly. It would be very difficult to give it up.

But this phase of my life was over. Campuses had to be left to young students and old professors—and guys like Terence Sproon. Now it was time to go to work.

Wednesday, May 15th, 1957
Ann Arbor

After I'd completed and mailed the employment application to Douglas Aircraft, they extended an offer to me at a salary of one hundred and thirty-two dollars a week. I accepted immediately.

I couldn't imagine what I was going to do with all that money. Owning a new Buick with an automatic transmission wasn't important any more. Besides, even with that big salary, I couldn't afford one since new cars were going for the unheard of price of two thousand dollars.

By midmorning, I had the Chevy all packed. Somehow, everything I owned fit into the car—something that would never happen again in my lifetime. Much of the backseat was taken up with stacks of my old engineering textbooks—Perry's *Aircraft Structures*, Timoshenko's *Strength of Materials*, Kaplan's *Advanced Calculus*, and all the rest.

I went around Owen House saying goodbye to everyone I could find.

Art Wilner, the lanky house steward from Kansas in charge of ordering the food, pressed a package of fig bars into my hand—a gift of appreciation for the blind date I had arranged for him in March. They were now going steady, even discussing marriage. Apparently, I had an even keener touch than Allen Rumsey's Nathan McCool for fixing people up with blind dates .

I shook hands with Yudi Balzar. For nearly three years, Yudi had kept his bayonet sheathed while pursuing his degree. His goodbye was laced with eloquent, multi-syllable English words.

In the kitchen Kozlovich put down his peanut butter sandwich and gave me a warm and tearful Russian bear hug.

"And be sure to show the new furnace man how to make shear pins *before* the house fills up with stoker gas," I told him. He nodded silently.

Jose Balderas, an eighteen-year-old freshman from Honduras, grasped my hand. "You lucky dog," he said in accented English. "You're getting away from this joint and starting a good job. If it weren't for my father wanting me to come up here for a dumb law degree, I'd be back home working in my uncle's packing plant in San Salvador—making good money and driving a red convertible. After this semester, that's it. I'm going back home no matter what he says."

"Don't be stupid," I said sharply. "Listen to your father—stick it out." I picked up one last armload of clothing and went out the door, leaving Balderas there to wonder what he'd said.

I climbed into the car, taking a long final look at Owen House. For months it had electrified the quiet neighborhood with an exterior coat of lime green paint. As last year's house manager, I had been instrumental in negotiating the special bargain price we'd gotten from a local paint dealer on twenty gallons of lime green. The old place didn't look half bad.

It started to drizzle as I pulled the Chevy away from the curb. Instead of heading south on Packard, I made a U-turn and went over to East University Avenue and north toward campus.

This was stupid, I thought. If I was going to make it down to New Mexico in time to get settled in before I started work on Monday, I should be on my way. But I had to take one last look around.

I stopped for the red light at East and South University Avenues. On the corner, the large, dark Engineering Arch cut through the West Engineering building at street level. Female students weren't considered bona fide coeds until they had been kissed under the arch. Regrettably, I'd never participated in that romantic tradition.

Further up East University was East Hall where freshman engineers still got their daily doses of compulsory English. Late spring was best for classes in East Hall. The steam radiators quit clanking when the weather got warmer.

On State Street, the Chevy's tires hissed drearily on the wet pavement. The State Theater was playing *Jet Pilot* with John Wayne and Janet Leigh. I used to catch all the John Wayne movies, but I'd missed the more recent ones.

I passed the Michigan Union building. These days there was talk about women wanting to gain access through the front entrance instead of going around to the side door, as tradition dictated. Some of the men—ones who had the time to get involved in campus politics—were resisting. Jack Radcliffe, my freshman orientation leader, would have thrived on leading this opposition, had he still been around.

I turned right, driving down Madison Street between the West and South Quads, birthplace of the now-infamous March 1952 panty raid, as well as the deathbed of our beloved 1940 Hudson that we'd driven up from White Sands in 1953.

I located my old dorm room window along the ivy-covered brick walls of Allen Rumsey House. Even though it was raining, the window was open. You could always get a good breeze through that window in the spring.

I wondered what had happened to my freshman roommates— Rosenkranz and Buttram. I hadn't heard from them in years. Rosenkranz was no doubt pulling in big bucks at some aircraft company, and Buttram was probably teaching music in a high school somewhere.

The guys hurrying through the rain in and out of the quadrangles looked so young. In fact, *everyone* around campus looked young these days.

I passed the P-Bell on Liberty Street. Glancing through the big side-walk windows, I saw lunchtime customers dining on the P-Bell's Wednesday-lunch special—German sausage and sauerkraut. It was too early in the day for serious beer drinking.

South Main Street took me past Michigan Stadium, home of the Michigan Wolverines. Michigan didn't have much of a football team while I'd been there, but I had faithfully attended every home game. Even during my freshman year, high above the end zone, I cheered them on, all the while guarding the empty seat next to me vacated by Bernice, my first campus sweetheart who jilted me when I ran out of conversation.

I needed a cup of coffee for the road, so I drove over to Red's Rite Spot on Williams Street.

I hadn't seen him for awhile, but Red nodded to me like I was just another daily customer. He brought the coffee over with a piece of fresh cherry pie and didn't give me a bill.

I didn't feel much like eating, but—what the hell—it was today's pie, so I pecked away at it until it was gone.

I looked over the jukebox selection. "You, You, You" wasn't there any more. I wondered if Ruth ever found a guy who measured up to her father's standards.

217

I told Red I was leaving. He nodded again. He'd seen lots of college students come and go. "Lemme know if you ever get tired of that engineering stuff," he said. "Good pot washers are hard to find."

I got on Packard Street and went south, heading for Route 66. I wanted to make three or four hundred miles yet that day before I had to pull over to catch some sleep on the front seat.

The rain was coming down harder now, and the wipers weren't clearing the windshield at all.

Perhaps it was the tears.

Epilogue

1997

March 1997
Marquette, Michigan

Iwent to work for Douglas Aircraft at White Sands in May 1957 and thoroughly enjoyed it. Ironically, in 1958, circumstances dictated my transfer to their missile facility in Santa Monica, California, where I found myself in a large hanger with hundreds of other faceless engineers. Shortly thereafter I left the large hanger and Douglas Aircraft and joined The Ramo-Wooldridge Corporation in El Segundo, California, embarking on a lengthy aerospace career.

The bulk of my career—thirty-one years—was spent at The Aerospace Corporation, also in El Segundo. I spent the final years as a department manager in charge of verification and validation of Air Force satellite and launch vehicle computer software.

In 1983 I went back to college, taking evening courses. At age fifty-two, I was older than all the other students and most of the professors. The old man was right, they'll let you back into school no matter how old you are. Two years later I received a master's degree in systems management from the University of Southern California.

In 1993, at age sixty and after the publication of my first book, *Northern Reflections*, I took an early retirement from The Aerospace Corporation to devote full time and energy to writing. Two additional books have since been published—*Northern D'Lights* and *Northern Passages*. These books are humorous, nostalgic short stories based on my experiences growing up in Upper Michigan in the 1940's.

I went back to Ann Arbor recently. Owen House is still a co-op, but get this—*it's coeducational!* (Can you believe that, Dean Deborah Barker?) The trees in the front yard have grown so large you can scarcely see the house from the street—unfortunate because the exterior paint color is now a very conservative white. The coal stoker has long since been replaced by some type of automatic furnace.

But some things never change. The large kitchen gas stove is the same one we used forty years ago; and skim milk, peanut butter, and white bread are still the free food of choice.

The Michigan Union looks the same, but nowadays women come and go through the front entrance with impunity.

The West Quad hasn't changed much either, except the ivy has gotten thicker on the brick walls and it's also coeducational. (How do they work that?)

The P-Bell on Liberty Street is gone. I suppose chug-a-lugging is now an ancient lost art.

Red's Rite Spot on Williams Street is gone, too. I'll bet there isn't a single restaurant in Ann Arbor now where the owner will come over and stir your coffee with his thumb.

In 1995 I visited White Sands—now renamed White Sands Missile Range. It's larger and very visitor-friendly. At the front gate, armed M.P.'s smile at you congenially, and a valid driver's license will get you onto the base.

The old Headquarters Building is still the Headquarters Building, but the old Officers' Club is now office space for Personnel Relations. The blockhouse is now—get this—*a historic landmark*! You can even take photos of it. In the 1950's, M.P.s would have shot you for that.

The Enlisted Men's Mess isn't there anymore and neither is the little Quonset hut where we lived in '52 and '53. However, there are still many of the original Quonset-type structures around, including the missile-assembly building where the Viking liquid-oxygen tank landed after the explosion in 1954. The roof has been patched up.

Across from the Headquarters Building is an open-air museum displaying the missiles tested at White Sands during its remarkable past. I recognized many of them. They have a V-2—much smaller-looking sitting next to its larger grandchildren. It's showing signs of corrosion from some chemical in the concrete they poured into the rocket to keep the wind from blowing it over. I wish they'd fix it up. There aren't many of them left.

In 1996, after living in Southern California for thirty-eight years, I moved back to Upper Michigan and am currently living in Marquette. So far this winter we've received twenty-one feet of snow. I'd forgotten how many things can go wrong with a car during an Upper Michigan winter.

As age advanced on him, my father began suffering a variety of ailments, finally going into a nursing home in his late eighties. One evening in

1984, while my mother was at his bedside, he took her hand and said to her, "I love you." Those were his last words. He was eighty-nine.

Just this last month my mother peacefully passed away at age ninety-five.

I have my parents to thank for my education, this book, and a fulfilled and interesting life. Left up to me, I'd be a retired tool and die maker now—every seven or eight years buying a new Buick with one of those newfangled automatic transmissions.

The writing was my own idea though, and it's been a happy choice as a second career.

I expect that the old man may be looking down on me and saying, "Writin? Any money in that?"

JERRY HARJU was born in Ishpeming, Michigan, in 1933. He received a degree in engineering mechanics from the University of Michigan in 1957 and completed his formal education with a MS from the University of Southern California in 1985. After thirty years as a manager in the aerospace industry in Southern California, Jerry began writing as a second career. His other books are *Northern Reflections, Northern D'Lights* and *Northern Passages:* collections of humorous short stories about his experiences growing up in Michigan's Upper Peninsula. He now lives in Marquette, Michigan, spending his time writing books and newspaper columns and travelling all over the globe. His travels include leading fly-in tours to Canada's high arctic, Greenland and the North Pole.